HAVE YOURSELF A MERRY LITTLE CHRISTMAS STORY

HAVE YOURSELF A MERRY LITTLE CHRISTMAS STORY

JOHN SCALLY

Ballpoint Press

To the memory of Jim Moran S.J.

"What we have once enjoyed, we can never lose.
All that we love deeply becomes part of us."
Helen Keller

Published in 2017 by Ballpoint Press
4 Wyndham Park, Bray, Co Wicklow, Republic of Ireland
Telephone: 00353 86 821 7631
Email: ballpointpress1@gmail.com
Web: www.ballpointpress.ie

ISBN 978-0-995479364

Book design and production by Joe Coyle Media&Design,
joecoyledesign@gmail.com

Printed and bound by GraphyCems

Contents

Introduction

SOME old customs can momentarily transfigure our existence and let the eternal shine through. One such custom is the singing of carols. They strike me as simple ways of expressing those parts of Christianity that ordinary people find most interesting, not the parts that people ought to find most interesting. They are memorable because they are so tangible. They celebrate things that we can touch and see and warm to: a mother and a baby, though curiously not a father, or at least not a real father, a stable, donkeys, shepherds, straw and hay.

As a boy growing up in Roscommon learning these carols did have a practical value because I could sing them on Wren Boys' Day. On St Stephen's Day children dressed up in old clothes with blacking and Red Indian-style daubs of lipstick on our faces and cycled to all the houses for miles around, where we sang, or more often wailed, in the confident expectation that we would be rewarded with a few coins for my musical offering. If there is ever a war crimes tribunal introduced for crimes against music I will rot in prison for eternity for the way I massacred that most beautiful Carpenters' song Top of the World.

Motley groups appeared on the roads or laneways looking like gangs of tramps in their assorted rags, faces masked or blackened. They did a jig or reel or sang a song, trying to disguise their voices, clinking the coins in their collection tins, chorussed their thanks and were on the way to make more money.

Despite my huge admiration for Charles Dickens my favourite Christmas story is a true story of the Wren Boys' Day. My good friend Paddy Joe Burke is a local legend because of his devotion to the Roscommon football team. He was not born with a silver spoon. When he was just a young boy his father died leaving a large family of hungry mouths too feed. It was the best of times. It was the worst of times. The family were poor materially but in terms of love and affection they were millionaires. Friday though was the most important day of the week for the household because it was the day the widow's pension was distributed. When he was eight Paddy Joe went 'on the Wren' and made a fortune by his standards of six shillings and eleven pence. That evening he stored it in his version of a safe. He put all the money in an old sock and wrapped it up and hid it in the hen house. That night he could barely sleep with the excitement, thinking of all the terrific treats that his windfall would allow him to buy in the coming year.

His mother always tried to put on a brave face but the next morning she was uncharacteristically subdued. It was a Tuesday morning and nobody knew what was wrong. Suddenly she got up from her chair and burst into tears. It was three full days until Friday and she had no money for food for the family after trying to make it a good Christmas for all the children. Immediately Paddy Joe rushed out to the hen house and raced back with the sock full of money. His mother's eyes lit up like a lighthouse in a storm. Paddy Joe had saved the day and the family would have enough to get through until Friday. Within a few minutes his oldest brother was sent off on his bicycle with the sock in one hand to buy a loaf of bread and some other essentials. When he came home with this 'feast' his mother never looked as happy. Paddy Joe has accomplished a lot in his life but he considers his greatest achievement to be the smile he put on his mother's face that Christmas.

To me this little story sums up the magic of Christmas – the one season when we all understand that if all we think of is number one we are not going to add to very much. It's a thrilling time for giving and for getting, a time for forgiving and for forgetting.

The stories in this book celebrate the unique magic that is Christmas. I hope they will provide a smile or two.

Foreword
By Fr Peter McVerry

SANTA is a person of utterly selfless generosity, who gives without expecting anything in return, except the satisfaction of knowing that he has given happiness to the children of this world. Santa never judges anyone; even those children who were bold do not get rejected, but they too receive their gifts from him. He inspires a group of little followers who work all year to get the presents ready so that children everywhere can laugh on Christmas day; they have committed themselves to the same selfless generosity as Santa himself. Even Rudolf and the other animals give him their undivided loyalty and do his bidding. Santa's little community is focused on bringing happiness to others.

Santa is the spirit of Christmas, as every child knows. Christmas without Santa would be a Christmas without magic. And Christmas without magic would be a Christmas without meaning. The stories in this book talk of the magic that is Christmas and the smiles of the children when the magic happens.

But for some, Christmas is a time of misery and struggle. Those who are lonely experience their aloneness more acutely at Christmas time, as they think of happy families opening their presents on Christmas morning. Some parents struggle, and end up drowned in debt, to try and bring a smile to the faces of their children on Christmas morning. Christmas is a very busy time for Childline, as children seek someone to whom they can express their unhappiness. The stories in this book also talk of the misery that is Christmas for some and the heroic struggles of some parents to make the magic happen for their children, against all the odds.

This book captures the whole reality of Christmas, both the wonder of Christmas time and the injustice in our world that condemns so many to poverty.

Acknowledgements

THANKS to Fr Peter McVerry for his support of this book.

Special thanks to Don Conroy for his help with illustrations and to Sarah Conroy for her involvement.

I am deeply grateful to PJ and Rosemary Cunningham and all at Ballpoint Press for their interest and professionalism.

I am again very indebted to Brian Flannery for supporting the book in a very practical way. Ruth Douglas has again been very helpful with this venture.

As always my good friend John Littleton has been a tower of strength and assistance.

My great friend Colm McGlynn has been a great support in a very tangible way at this time.

I am keenly appreciative of the generous support the Davy Group have consistently given the Peter McVerry Trust. My particular thanks to Ian Brady for his support of the work of the trust.

Thanks to the legend that is Paddy Joe Burke for sharing his story with me. Another Roscommon legend Seamus Hayden was characteristically generous with his support and kindly placed the famous 'Down the Hatch' at my disposal.

Thanks too to Mary Kennedy, Ollie Campbell and Paul Earley for their help with the project.

The queen of the Inner City Elizabeth 'Betty' O'Shea has been in my thoughts and prayers as this book was being written.

So too was my good friend Patricia Dennehy. I wish her every blessing in this exciting new chapter in her life.

In her 95th year Margarete Anna Sundermann, a much loved mother and grandmother, left us as this book was almost finished. May she rest in peace.

Margaret Coll continues to be a luminous lamp of light and love in Donegal.

Every good wish to Marie Therese Pierce as she embarks on a new stage of her life journey.

A great oak has fallen in the theological forest with the passing of Vincent MacNamara in July. His confrères in the Kiltegan Fathers will miss him deeply.

While this book was being completed Iarlaith Creggy was born into the loving family of Claire, JP and Niamh. Likewise Sophie Hogan defied the odds to bring new rays of love into the world for her sisters Lizzy and Hannah.

Philomena Molloy has faced a tough year with courage, grace and dignity. Fiona Maher has also fought the good fight this year.

My very particular thanks to our wonderful designer Joe Coyle who generously donated his services on foot of his deep admiration for Fr Peter.

John Scally
October 2017

One

Oh No. Not You Again

HE was a man who had suffered a great wound, an unseen wound, because all the pain was inside him.

They called him 'Not You Again'. It was because of the mat outside his front door which read: 'Not You Again'. To be fully correct it actually read: 'Oh No. Not you Again.' His name was Ben and his tongue was so sharp and precise he could slice bacon with it. His fingers were stained with nicotine, and he twitched a lot as though the absence of a cigarette in his hand was messing with a mind already carrying an unwieldy emotional elixir around inside him.

It was not that he had a superiority complex. He simply thought he was better than everyone else by virtue of his birth. As a boy one of the big events of his life was when his father took him on the train to Dublin on the eighth of December for Christmas shopping. An exotic looking man with sallow skin sat opposite them on the train. Ben could not help himself but he asked this strange looking creature where he was from. His father kicked him furiously under the table in a clear signal to shut up. When they got to Grafton Street Ben finally plucked up the courage to ask his reticent father what he had done wrong. First his father sighed. Then he slowly shook his head before saying with the weight of conviction: 'If he's from Cork he will say so and if he's not you're only embarrassing him.'

At school Ben was a scholarship boy and was one of the lucky ones to get a place on a teacher training course in Saint Patrick's College in Drumcondra. One of his classmates, John McGahern, would find fame in the world of literature and put Leitrim on the map in the process.

In contrast Ben found himself teaching in a primary school in Limerick. At the time he believed that the biggest cultural force in the city were the Redemptorists. For Ben as a young man the interaction with the Redemptorists mainly came in his periodic excursions into the confessional box. His first encounter unfolded as follows:

'Bless me Father for I have sinned. It was Christmas since I made my last confession.'

'Tell me your sins my son.'

'I had bad thoughts Father.'

'And tell me did you entertain them.'

'I'm afraid it's more serious than that Father.'

'I'm sorry my son I'm confused. Please explain what you mean.'

'I'm afraid they entertained me.'

'And have you any other sins?'

'I have been drinking Father.'

'How much do you drink my son?'

'I don't drink normally and I don't normally drink.'

The human heart is a strange thing. Did even God understand his creation? Ben's level of abrasiveness toned down after his marriage to Sheila even though he often joked: 'Life's a bitch and I married her.'

She was a constant surprise to him. She could ask him: 'A small leak can sink a ship. You know who said that?'

'No.'

'Neither do I.'

Another of her comments was: 'The curtains were drawn but the furniture was real.'

Then there was her moments of insight and wisdom: 'Hang on tightly. Let go lightly.'

Ben's dark humour was not to her taste. There was that time

when they went shopping on Christmas Eve. They got separated and he rang her on her shiny new mobile which seemed to weigh half a ton. 'Do you remember that jewellers we went into last Christmas and you saw that fabulous necklace that I could not afford?', Ben asked.

'Yes, I do', she answered with a leaping heart.

'Well, I'm in the coffee shop next door to it.'

When she asked her husband if he would choose between ending world hunger or winning the lotto Ben answered, 'How many rooms can I have in my new mansion'.

Ben did not like the word pregnant so when his wife became with child he prayed for a period of safe confinement for her. He had taken in her scent, a smell he could conjure up perfectly to this day.

He had felt the danger coming, almost like how animals react so early to an approaching storm. When she was struck down by serious illness her breaths came in gusts, her face was grossly contorted, her forehead clammy, her nightdress soaked with perspiration as she gripped her rosary beads in her right hand, her mouth silently trying to recite the familiar words between screams of agonised pain. Ben had tried vainly to comfort her, not knowing if he should touch her, his hands seeming to feel huge and useless in his pockets. He flinched as he watched her face turn fish white, years older overnight and swollen with her pregnancy.

He believed the angels wept when the soul of an innocent dies. When the dreadful news emerged that his wife had died in childbirth a sudden anger flashed down his brain but instead of the expected storm breaking he controlled his rage first and simply said: 'In manus tuas, Dominie, commendo spiritum meum.'

Then the grief hit him like a bad drug as his heart sank to a depth he had not realized existed within him. Moaning, he fell back into a chair, wracking his frame to such a degree that he looked as though he would erupt like a volcano spewing forth for more misery than human beings had the ability to endure. This all came out like a blast of pent-up air finally released.

He had prayed to God that both would live. But sometimes God was busy with other things. This he knew to be true. God had been busy when he needed him most. But so many people needed God. He was just one of millions, probably billions, who had sought divine assistance the same day. Whether or not Ben interpreted this event as some divine signal was unclear. His actions, however, were crystal clear. Over the coming weeks he felt a deep sadness sucking him dry and persisting doggedly.

Her funeral had been on the morning of Christmas Eve. The weather was cold, the sky puffy with clouds. The wind cleaved the thickest coats. The roads were icy and treacherous. He had been driven to the cemetery in the funeral home car designated for family members. His father-in-law Simon rode up in front, next to the driver while he squeezed in the back with his mother-in-law and her sisters. The driver slowed the car where the road met the gravel, wary of the fallen branches that may have formed in the earlier storm. Even the most insignificant of those details still seemed significant all these years later.

The graveside service was mercifully brief, Father Dan seemed to understand that if he didn't speed things along, some of the older and frail people might not survive the cold. He had memorized every detail of the place. He could never forget where his wife and child were buried any more than he would ever fail to remember his own name.

Throughout Ben stared vacantly at the coffin. At one stage he put his hand on the casket, mumbled a few words, and pulled back, feeling totally disorientated. He had played this scene out in his head a million times in the coming years. Nothing about this was right. He felt he was staring at the world upside down as the child he never knew was lowered to the ground in a tiny white coffin. 'I'll be with you soon, Shelia', he said in a husky voice. The words sounded hollow, forced but he could think of nothing else to say. As he started to collapse, a strong hand gripped him. 'It's all right, Ben. We'll get you back to the car now.' He looked up into the face of his barber, Paddy Joe. He was driven home, the absence of Shelia in their midst, a festering wound that no possible healing medicine could alleviate.

He had never been able to forget things, no matter if he wanted to forget it or not. He could remember everything Shelia had ever worn, every body tic she ever made and most gallingly every row they had. He knew they were invariably his fault and that recognition haunted him. It was like ocean waves relentlessly pounding his tired mind. His guilt was numbing. He would sob anew each time he recalled his many angry exchanges with her. They were stupid little episodes that did not mean anything – an act replicated a thousand times over the life of many successful marriages, and yet those were his last memories of their lives together.

He liked to walk through rain. It seemed to help him think, his mind clearing even as the clouds above thickened. It did not make sense but it was as if he found some help from above.

It would not be true to say he always dreaded the thoughts of Christmas but it was in the margin of error because all the old memories it inevitably trespassed on. His standard Christmas greeting was: 'Here's to those who wish me well and those who don't can go to hell.'

When you have been to hell anything less does not intimidate you. Yet despite himself he made a bit of an effort to decorate his home every Christmas. This is part of the fabric of life. You tried to wipe out important things and replace them with other important things. These were lessons that never left him. They were mental scars carved on his brain and his soul. Love lodges not only in the heart but in the brain, and with the brain there are a myriad of feelings and memories, tangible threads to the precious woman he once loved.

He had sought unsuccessfully to substitute teaching for Shelia. There were times when it was a diverting distraction like when he tried to teach poor Padraig to count.

'Padraig you get two rugby balls, a pair of rugby balls, and a couple of rugby balls. How many rugby balls do you have?'

'Seven sir.'

'Seven! You fuc – you infuriating boy. How could you possibly get seven? Let's do this one more time. You get two rugby balls, a pair of rugby balls, and a couple of rugby balls. How many rugby balls do you have?'

'Seven sir.'

'Padraig, you would give an aspirin a headache. Let's try something else. You have two cricket balls, a pair of cricket balls, and a couple of cricket balls. How many do you have?'

'Six sir.'

'Padraig! You are a genius. But how could you get six that time and seven the first two times?'

'Ah sure, I have one rugby ball at home already sir.'

Ben's house was called 'Paradise', Sheila's idea. It was far larger than he needed but he had no interest in moving. This would be his last home. He had known that for a long time. He lived beside the Shannon river. On either side of his house was another house pretty much exactly the same. All of the estate was more or less exactly the same as if a builder had some large machine to spit the houses out off-site to later be transported and erected here.

For better or worse, much of him belonged to this house, even with all the pain it had caused. With Christmas coming that pain would become more intense and shrill. Ben sat in the parlour and gazed around the memories of a lifetime. He had a poster on the fridge which had a quote from G.K. Chesterton: 'Don't ever take a fence down until you know the reason it was put up.'

The maple bookcase seemed so out of place in this tired space. Most of the dusty volumes neatly lining the shelves seemed to be the novels of Jane Austen, George Eliot and Charles Dickens.

On the walls and shelters were photos of his late wife. His gaze rested longer on a picture of them together on their wedding day. It was a June afternoon when the sky was climbing high in the sky. It had been hot but the breeze was nice he recalled managing to evaporate several beads of sweat off his forehead. God, how long was it since he had worn such a wide smile? As he did religiously every day he made a sign of the cross over the picture on her own in the new, good dress he had brought for her for their first Christmas together as a married couple. It had seemed a ridiculous extravagance at the time because it had cost him two months wages but now he thought of it as his best investment because this was the way he would always remember her. The only good thing about her passing was that she would never age.

He looked sadly at the wedding ring on his left hand, the ring finger swollen by time so that the simple gold band would never come off without taking the digit off with it. Sometimes, he thought, living was far harder than dying. Increasingly he found himself quoting Woody Allen's quip: "I'm not afraid of death, I just don't want to be there when it happens."

On a snowy evening Ben set off to buy his Christmas shopping. Something deep inside him wanted a return to the Christmases of innocence. He took down his overcoat. He was tall but bent. His spine had curved itself over the last decade and that reduced his height by two inches. Yet even under his grey coat, the bulky strength of his shoulders and chest were evident. His hair was cut short and in severe lines around his face which had all the tracks of sun damage one would expect after more than seven decades of living. Although still physically strong mentally and emotionally he was not doing very well. He wasn't sure he ever would be doing well ever again. Some days he thought he would, others not. This was one of the other days in the circle and loop of memories. He just wanted to be doing something that would transport him to the future rather than always carry him back to the past. Thought has wings and Ben was no stranger to the tricks the mind can play.

He trundled though the thickening snow and headed for the local Dunnes Stores. An old man, still wheezing from the awkward walk up the steps, was shivering on the bridge, braced against the railing, wondering if he would make it for another year. The spray of water is beautiful on the railings. Splendid and theatrical. The sky above the spray was the darkest the man had ever seen. He stood shakily watching the physical and psychic eyesore of stalled construction, additions that would never be completed, apartment complexes aborted even before the windows got their glass as the economic crash swopped on the Celtic Tiger like a hawk.

For some unknown reason Ben found himself in the Abbey Book Shop and looking at all the religious items on display. His eye was caught by a beautiful crib and it seemed to have mesmerised him. A smiling assistant, with a twinkle in her eye, approached him and said:

'It's lovely isn't it? Are you interested?

'My teacher's pension doesn't pay me enough to afford that.'

'You're a teacher.'

'I was.'

'So is my son. You still want that crib.'

'Like I said it's not on my budget.'

'How much can you afford?'

'Twenty euro.'

'Then today is your lucky day.'

'Can you do that?'

'I just did.'

'I appreciate that.'

'No. I appreciate you.'

She wrapped up the crib beautifully and Ben headed home with an extra bounce in his step. When he unwrapped it he found that there were two figures of the baby Jesus in the manger. He immediately went back to the shop to see if they had any cribs which were missing a baby Jesus. But there was none. So he wrote a little note and posted it in the window which stated: 'If you are missing the baby Jesus call to: Paradise, 57 Castlebrook.'

Days passed and Ben forgot all about it. Then at 6.28 p.m. on Christmas Eve there was a very timid knock at the door just as he was making the gravy for his feast of roast potatoes, goose and stuffing with mince pies for desert that were making him salivate. He frowned severely as he opened the door but his heart melted as he saw a shivering, thin woman holding a tiny bundle whose eyes were scrunched shut, clutched in her arms. The moonlight drifted through the window, giving shape to certain objects in the darkened internal of the frame. He spotted immediately that although she was poorly dressed for the cold her baby was well wrapped up.

Ben eyed her with an incredulous look. All he could say was: 'Can I help you Miss?'

She leaned in so close that Ben could smell her breath. Tears welled up in her eyes. There were dark curls under those eyes and recently stamped worry lines on her face. The glow had gone from her skin. Her gaze was downcast, her look one of lost confidence. Her brow was a mass of premature wrinkles.

A part of her wanted this man to look at her, another part of her did not. She did not want to see pity in his eyes. This bright, intelligent young woman reduced to this. She said: 'I'm sorry to bother you Mister. I saw your notice in the shop window and I had nowhere else to go. I don't mind if I have to stay out in the cold but I don't want my baby Paulie to be sleeping in the open on Christmas Eve. Could you give us any help please? I'm sorry I should have said my name is Shauna by the way.'

Her words were spoken in a supremely tired manner. Ben could almost feel the incredible strain in her timbre. It had taken a supreme effort at self-control, as she held her head up and attempted to talk normally. She took a long breath and tried to smile.

Ben felt like an axe had melted his frozen heart and he invited Shauna and Paulie in out of the cold and to share his meal with him. He motioned to her to follow him into the kitchen. She closed the door and dutifully trudged in after him. She had black hair. However, she had clearly dyed it, several times with different colours over the years and Ben had no idea what word best described it now.

Ben prepared hot milk for her infant child who had woken up. His eyes were wide open and the brightest of blues and the toddler formed a small and contented hump on her mother's chest. Ben invited them to stay for Christmas. Shauna seemed the first person in ages who could meet Ben's eyes without hesitation. They seemed to burn through the external wall he had constructed around himself.

As he tossed and turned in his bed that night Ben reflected: 'You should respect the past. You should never forget the past. But you can't live there.'

Two

The Best Teacher Ever

KATY DOBEY won the award for the best teacher every year because apart from her great love of teaching and her deep love of her students she had the kindest heart. She could cope confidently with the boundless energy of junior infants that would send others looking for the ulcer medicine, with worry lines prominent on their forehead.

Teaching could suck up every ounce of energy and intellectual curiosity one cared to give it. Katy though had an uncanny ability to work through the small, seismic vibrations of childhood and in unmeasurable infinitesimal increments sculpt a hidden treasure. The years of wrestling with recalcitrant infants had honed her skills of cajoling and consoling. She could read their thoughts.

Whenever somebody invited her to lunch she would send them the most beautiful Disney thank you card afterwards with the cutest picture of Bambi on the front. It stated: 'Kind people are like flowers. They make the world wonderful.'

Because of her striking good looks and her even sweeter nature her home was nicknamed 'Beauty Central'. Nobody who knew her could say it did not fit given the goodness of her character. Her patience with her students and love for them was infinite. Her clothes were always stylish and elegant and she wore them with effortless elan. She had an athletic grace, which made her such a good dancer. Her smile was infectious but yielded in its impact to her dancing blue eyes.

On her classroom wall was a poster, which read:
'Talk to yourself at least once a day.
Otherwise you may miss an excellent person in this world.'
On the other wall was a poster which read:

Do all the good you can
By all the means you can
In all the ways you can
In every place you can
All the times you can
To all the people you can
As long as ever you can.

Everyone had choices to make and Katy had made her own. She lived by the philosophy that the one who sets about making others better is wasting their time, unless they begin with themselves.

On the day of the Christmas holidays Katy had been up early to wrap with love her presents for her fantastic family she loved so much. She also bought selection boxes for each student in her class.

She smiled to herself as she recalled yesterday's class. She had asked everybody in the class how they celebrated Christmas Eve. Mary O'Toole was first up she answered with breathless excitement: 'Teacher, teacher, I get a glass of milk and a piece of chocolate cake and some candy canes and I leave them on a chair beside the tree for Santa and then I go to bed very early because when Santa is making his list and checking it twice I want to be with the good girls.'

Katy had nodded her head wisely and said, 'That is lovely Mary.'

Next to reply was the effusively effervescent Ciara Sanchez. 'Teacher, teacher. I leave a carrot for Rudolph beside the chimney and some mince pies and lemonade for Santa Claus and I put up my stocking beside the tree to have it ready for all my presents. Then I go to bed early so Santa will know I am a good girl.'

And on and on it went until finally it got to the last student Rachel Briscoe, the only Jewish girl in the class who said: 'Teacher,

teacher. Our chauffeur takes us all to Daddy's toy factory. Then when they see that all the shelves are empty my Mammy and Daddy open a big bottle of champagne and give a toast to the baby Jesus. Then we go the airport and fly first class to New York and spend the holidays in our penthouse suite in a luxury hotel in Manhattan.'

Outside the dark clouds were heavy with moisture. On the car radio into work she listened to Ireland's best music programme by a country mile the Gareth O'Callaghan show. There was a surprise for Katy when the principal in her primary school in west Dublin decided she would have a competition for each class. Beside the beautiful, big Christmas tree in the school hall she put a lovely basket of Christmas treats: full of sweets, chocolate and little gifts. Each class would have a race and whoever got there first won the Christmas basket. It would all be the most delightful appetizer for the festivities that would come over the Christmas holidays. A cloud passed and the light of the sun suddenly lit up the room as if to rejoice at the news.

There was great excitement when all of the classes heard this and the cheer that went up nearly lifted the roof. The students were exceptionally excited and somewhat difficult to control.

Parents and grandparents were in attendance. When a man of massive girth walked in front of her, Katy's attention was instantly riveted upon him even though he barged by without a backward glance. A corpulent red face housed light blue eyes hiding behind lids reduced to slits by sagging facial skin and the overgrowth of a pair of eyebrows as thick as she had ever seen. His hair and beard was white and abundant, the nose was wide and the tip was even redder than the rest of his face. For one brief moment Katy wondered if she was confronting Santa Claus. She was mildly surprised but did not show it.

The principal decided that they would start with sixth class and work down. The races were very exciting and in each class there was one very happy student as they ate all their lovely treats.

Finally it was the turn of Katy's Junior Infants class who were almost hyper in their excitement. They looked intense and determined. They would have to be to survive this thought the principal. But when she called for the start of the race she got a big surprise.

When Katy told the students to run, they all took each other's hands and ran together, so that each of them won the race in a dead heat. Then they sat down together and enjoyed their treats and a festive feeling pervaded the air. Every adult pair of eyes in the school hall stared at Katy as if she was the repository of secrets, or at least this secret.

The principal asked Katy why they had run like that when one could have kept all the treats for themselves, her curiosity was clearly evident in her voice, which had a slight hitch that was compelling in its disclosure of what she was really thinking. A twitch in her right eye showed that this day was not going according to plan. Katy answered: 'I teach them that one of us can not be happy if all the other ones are sad. The heart of Christmas is, "I am because we are".'

It was not the words she used that had impressed her principal. You could find something like them in any Hallmark aisle. It was how she said them, with utter conviction in her voice, and even more tellingly in her dancing blue eyes. It was always the eyes that gave Katy away. In terms of both recognition and emotion her eyes were the windows into her soul.

Her face flushed with pleasure the principal thanked Katy for teaching her an invaluable Christmas lesson. Silence lingered for a few heartbeats. The principal swallowed a couple of times to work through the dryness in her throat before saying in a voice choked with emotion: 'It's Christmas the time of miracles.'

This was not the first time she had said this. Yet for some reason her spirits soared for a moment.

There was a twinkle in her eye as Katy replied: 'Every time a hand reaches out to help another that is Christmas. Every time someone puts anger aside and strives for understanding that is Christmas. Every time people forget their conflicts and differences and realize their love for each other that is Christmas.'

As he listened to Bing Crosby singing 'White Christmas' on his old cassette player, his black habit swirling around his thick white ankles, he looked forward to the moment when his festivities really began as the bells chimed to announce it was midnight and as he watched the lights gleaming from homes that would usually be in darkness

Three

The Silver Spoon

CHRISTMAS was always a magical time of the year for Br Tom. He loved the crisp chill of winter evenings and the sharp smell of burning logs over fires in a hundred hearths not to mention the almost sinful sensory scents of Christmas cakes baking. He thought he could see a dim rectangle of light in the distance. The abbot had clearly managed to light a candle, and its little flame filled the hall with eerily dancing shadows. It was not that the abbot was mean he just treated every penny like a prisoner.

Raising his eyebrows in amusement he loved the atmosphere of anticipation and excitement as the townspeople streamed from their snug warm homes to attend Midnight Mass in the Church with dozens of bells chiming and clanging to herald the special occasion and a hundred late worshippers hurrying to be on time, and he adored the candlelit naves and the heady smell of smoky incense as it drifted in a white smoky pall.

As he listened to Bing Crosby singing White Christmas on his old cassette player, his black habit swirling around his thick white ankles, he looked forward to the moment when his festivities really began as the bells chimed to announce it was midnight and as he watched the lights gleaming from homes that would usually be in darkness. His sister Mary had lovingly crafted a huge plum cake, which would be savoured with slices of creamy yellow cheese after the Mass with some mulled wine to wash it down. He was not the only one in the monastery to appreciate the heat from the hearth or to welcome the warmth of a glass of mulled wine in his hands.

He loved to hear the voices of excited children talking about Santa Claus and the choir practicing their singing of ancient songs and struggling to master their annual new addition to their set list. He even had a wry smile last year when he found a man lying full length on his front, arms flung out above his head, as though he had caught his foot in a pothole and had fallen flat on his face. His collar was askew and his breathing deep and loud. The unmistakable smell of whisky was thick in the air around him.

It seemed colder than normal that evening, and the wind sliced more keenly through Br Tom's clothes. The cloisters lovely though they were, comprised a lattice of carved stone that did little to the brisk breeze that rushed in from the north east. He loved to stand in the nave in the mornings, listening to the chanting, closing his eyes to appreciate the singing as it washed and echoed along the vaulted roof as the first rays of sunlight caught the bright glass in the windows. Invariably they made dappled patterns in red, yellow and blue on the smooth cream paving stones of the monastery floor.

As he headed towards the refectory a few confreres walked briskly past him, chattering together as they walked, but most were silent, each wrapped in their own thoughts, their dark robes swinging about their legs as they hurried towards the delicious buttery smell of baked potatoes and onion soup. It seemed every available scrap of wall space was covered in brilliantly hued paintings, and every niche boasted a statute of a saint, the flagstones were bare and, apart from a rather expensive-looking altar, there was not another piece of furniture in evidence. He spotted the familiar figure of Br Matthew with his tousled hair and a liberal collection of freckles clutching his rosary beads as he sliced a decadently large piece of pecan pie. Br Patrick was lecturing to a group of novices, using his hands to illustrate the point, as was his wont. His nickname was the windmill because his arms were always wheeling around like sails in the wind.

As evening approached, the clouds thinned, so that flashes of golden sun started to break through them. By dusk, they had fragmented to the point where there were only a few banks left, each one tinged salmon pink as the sun began to set. Cheered by the sight of a clear sky after so many overcast days, Br Tom wandered into the yard, and watched the bright orange globe sink behind the trees at the bottom of the garden. The clouds seemed more vividly painted than he had ever seen them before; they glowed amber and scarlet, before fading to the shade of dull embers and then to a misty purple as darkness fell.

Br Tom headed towards the homeless hostel he ran on behalf of his Congregation. He grabbed his warmest winter cloak and swung it over his shoulders. Against the chilly darkness of the night, the lights from the Church formed a welcoming glow. He could hear the distant voices of the elderly monks on the breeze as they finished reciting the office of compline and readied themselves for bed.

The hostel locks were the best money could buy and would have been difficult to force but he had the Brother Superior's keys, and the well-oiled clasps snapped open instantly. Br Tom occupied a cramped office and stifled a sigh of annoyance at the lack of space. Nonetheless it was a pleasant room, filled with golden floors, which were tastefully decorated with tapestries and rugs.

Br Tom was commendably discreet and peerless at giving the comforting impression that no one would ever learn about a private meeting or conversation from him. That was why all the visitors to the hostel felt comfortable talking to him. He first spoke that evening with Micky Joe who was shaking his head in tolerant resignation. Unfortunately, his eccentric way of moving as he talked to himself meant that he was seldom taken seriously outside the hostel. Normally he was compliant and patient, but Christmas made him agitated and moody, oscillating between angry defiance and frightened tearfulness. Anxiety was written clearly on his pallid face that had survived over eighty Christmases. Br Tom was anxious to do what little he could to alleviate the uneasy atmosphere and asked Mickey Joe what he would like for Christmas. 'A spoon,' was the surprising answer. Momentarily thrown Br Tom said, 'You are very low maintenance Mickey Joe. You look frozen let's go and get you some of the nice hot stew that Br Mark has been slaving over all afternoon.'

Mickey Joe savoured every mouthful of the delicious meal. He was first in the line on Christmas Day for the much anticipated Christmas lunch which again he relished. There was a nice surprise for him after the enticing desert of mince pies and cream when Br Tom approached him and presented him with a gift wrapped in lovely Christmas paper and with an impressive red bow. After he gasped his thanks Mickey Joe opened the present which was a silver spoon. Mickey Joe smiled his thanks before tears toppled in steady streams down his cheeks.

Br Tom's dark eyes took in the scene with undisguised curiosity and he said, 'Mickey Joe, please excuse my vulgar curiosity but why did you want a spoon for Christmas? I know you have to take a lot of tablets. Is it because a spoonful of sugar makes the medicine go down?'

Mickey Joe laughed heartily at first before almost being choked by a fit of wheezing coughing, 'No. The reason I wanted the spoon is that every time we have meals here whenever I see a spoon I know that something nicer is to come after we finish our main meal. I am not long for this world. We both know it will be you who will have to arrange my funeral because I have nobody who will miss me apart from you. When I die I want you to put the spoon with me in my coffin.'

'I don't understand', said Br Tom.

'The spoon is a symbol for me that something better is to come. That is the message of Christmas that a child is born with a promise to the world of better things to come. That is the message that I want to take with me to my grave.'

Four
The Christmas Dinner

TINY Tommy was now eight years old. On the first of July he had written his letter to Santa Claus. He had asked for two Christmas presents this year – a carpenter's set and a builder's set.

On Christmas Eve as always he had a pizza from the local takeaway with his parents for lunch as his mother prepared for the Christmas dinner of turkey, ham, stuffing, roast potatoes and mice pies for the next day.

Well not exactly as always because this was the first year that his grandfather had not joined them for lunch on Christmas Eve. Tiny Tommy's grandfather was getting very old and he had started to dribble his food a little when he ate his meals. Both Tommy's father and mother had got very upset when he did this. Then during the year they had got so annoyed that they built a new extension to their house and put Tommy's grandfather into it – so that he could have all his meals in there all by himself and they would never have to watch him eat and dribble his food ever again. For his part Tiny Tommy was usually perfectly happy to relax in the company of adults, despite their peculiarities. But at this news he was mortified, and hung his head in embarrassment. But his grandfather was unabashed, and dealt with the insult with cool dignity but his son did not relent in the face of his disarming graciousness.

Tommy's father had a face that was plumper than it should have been for a man of his age, and there were bulges above his hips that testified to too much good living. His hands were pale and soft, as though he scorned any sort of activity that would harden them, and there was almost a decadent air about him. His clothes presented a stark contrast to the other man of the house. Whereas

Tommy's grandfather wore shirts that were frayed and patched, his father's were new and the height of fashion. As he turned his languorous gaze upon his wife his beard was in the peculiar style that covered the chin and upper lip, but left the sides of the face clean shaven.

It was the smell of the house that Tommy's grandfather had liked best. It was warm and welcoming, a mixture of freshly baked bread from the kitchen, and of the slightly bitter aroma of burning wood. His daughter-in-law had decorated it with flowers, and vases stood here and there, mingling their sweet fragrance with the scents already in the room. As it was dark, lamps were lit, filling the room with a warm amber glow. The house had until now always brought back pleasant memories for him.

The old man did not give the impression that he was bound for the pearly gates, although everybody imagined that he was more likely to be admitted than anyone else they knew. His son, however, exuded the sense that he already had one foot and several toes through the heavenly portals, and that he felt sorry for everyone else because they did not. His eyes shone with the light of the saved. His wife had a similar attitude, although it was less flagrant.

Tommy's mother seemed spellbound by the kitchen walls which were painted pale pink. In the flattering half-light of the fire and the lamps, it seemed that the years had been kind to her. She had been an intense young woman in her twenties in UCD when she had first started to make a name for herself in the university with her scholarship. However, her face had retained its smooth skin and her brown hair was unmarked by grey; these, combined with her slight, girlish build, had led many an academic adversary to underestimate her in the debating chamber. Such opponents did not make that mistake a second time. Her belligerence and single-mindedness made her unpopular with the students, but they had to admit that standards had risen since she became head of the French Department. She wore huge buttons on her jacket. When her husband remarked: 'If one of those things bounces upwards, it will take you teeth out', she looked at him with characteristic arched eyebrows. Whenever she met a man for the first time she looked him up and down in a brazen assessment of his physique.

On Christmas morning Tiny Tommy woke early and rushed down the stairs to check under the Christmas tree. He let out a great squeal of excitement. Although he woke up his parents they did not complain.

That morning at breakfast Tommy's dad asked him what he was going to do with the new carpenter's and builder set. With his eyes shining Tommy told them that he was going to build a new extension to their house. Puzzled by Tommy's answer his father asked him why he wanted to build a new extension to their house.

With complete innocence he answered: 'So I can put you and Mammy in there once you get old and I will never have to go near you again.'

Tommy's mother was so shocked by his answer that she let one of the cups aunt Margaret had given her as a wedding present fall out of her hands and smash in tiny pieces on the floor.

She looked deep into her husband's eyes. The snow was still coming down, although the latest weather report had said that with the temperatures staying where they were, it would be more likely to be ice than snow over Christmas.

When my father died ten months later, my grandfather became possibly the most important person in my life. I was called after him. Even his birthday was the same as mine. With his grey hair, weather-beaten face, commanding presence and enormous eyelashes, he was not a man to take lightly

Five

Five

The Proposal

IT was the most magical Christmas Eve ever.

I was four and I had been surprised to see that my father was gone to town in the morning.

"You are going to get a big surprise this evening" my grandmother told me mysteriously. My mind ran wild with the possibilities as I went out with my grandfather to look after the sheep. The chill of the late afternoon made me shiver as I pulled my heavy coat around me. The winter that year had been cold and stormy. The gales began in late November, seeming to follow each other, with brief interludes until the end of the following April.

"You can tell what a winter will be like by the weather on the first of November" my father always said. I have put that theory to the test every year since he died. As a rule of thumb it is pretty good.

There was a lull that day in the winter-long storm. The sky was blue but there were battalions of black clouds on the horizon westward which were irrefutable evidence that snow was on its way. The low sun seemed to shiver in the ranging northern wind. It was an admission of defeat. Normally, on a winter afternoon with darkness due and snow-clouds threatening I would have not been allowed out. With both my parents in town my grandfather needed the little assistance I could provide. This was no day to leave an unseasonally early lambing ewe to nature.

"God its quare cauld. That cold could kill any baby lamb. Nature is cruel." said my grandfather uncomfortably, as if his teeth were chattering in the icy air. The wind chill factor must have been in operation. There were a dozen ruins scattered here and there around the fields. The sheep sheltered behind those walls in bad weather, as it often was at the time of the year. If young lambs survive in the cold, it is the old wisdom of their mothers that preserves them finding a snug place for them to shelter.

We searched long and hard before we found the final ewe. She was hiding under a furze bush. Thankfully my grandfather had the foresight to bring a flash-lamp with him. By then the snow clouds had come in from the west and before we knew it we were enveloped in a blizzard. I wanted to take shelter like the flock, behind some wall. My grandfather answered my plea with a hard look, and silence. He would not allow us to be exiled by the snow and took me up in his arms as if I was a precious jewel and ploughed an uneven furrow through the already ankle-deep snow. I had never known such cold. Although the north wind nearly cut him in two, he was happy to feel it. It meant the snow clouds would be kept on the move. The warm house awaited us like a sanctuary. Thankfully the snow had stopped. The air was quiet again though another barrage of blue-black clouds were looming ominously on the western horizon. There would be more snow within the hour. The outside light looked more festive and welcoming than even the tinsel-coloured Christmas tree in the parlour window.

As we stumbled in the door I saw my father putting on his wellingtons to head out to find us. He whisked me out of my grandfather's arms and deposited me in front of the range where he began to rub me vigorously to get my circulation going again. The relief on his face and in his voice that we were both safe was palpable. There was a mountain of snowflakes on our clothes and wellingtons. A pool of water formed on the floor as the moisture condensed.

Whenever I was out with him in the fields in the cold he always kept my hands warm by clapping my hands together and reciting three times:

"Clap handins, clap handins till Daddy comes home
with sweets in his pocket for John alone."

What I remember most about that evening was that he changed the rhyme, as he beamed down at me clapping my hands together.

"Clap handins, clap handins till Daddy comes home with a television in the car for John alone."

Then I saw it in the corner, a brand new television. I knew the amount of saving and scraping that had gone into buying it. I felt special, honoured like a prince. I believed he had got the television especially for me. I felt a lump in my throat. I heard myself saying "I love you Daddy". He was surprised but pleased. I was not sure which of us was the happiest. The happiness was shared by all the family. There was the special atmosphere normally only achieved on Christmas night.

When my father died ten months later my grandfather became possibly the most important person in my life. I was called after him. Even his birthday was the same as mine. With his grey hair, weather-beaten face, commanding presence and enormous eyelashes, he was not a man to take lightly. His attraction to frugal living would have made him a kindred spirit for an ascetic. He was a devout man. I wondered if he ever stepped down from this heightened plain of spiritual existence to the world of mere mortals. Once I asked him:

"Will you ever be a saint, Grandpa?"

The question amused him. Although he answered with an emphatic "No!" it failed to prompt the series of singular revelations half-hoped for.

He was the eldest of thirteen children, born to a farmer who owned only five acres of land. It was a life of extreme poverty though he did not know it at the time. It was a world before television and radio. He thought it was great. I remember him telling me, "If you are reared in your bare feet you will never get pneumonia out of the snow."

Looking back he was convinced that what had sustained him

through the years was a belief in God. Raking hay with him one day, when he was talking about the old days, he admitted in a moment of exceptional candour:

"When I was young the only reason I ever wanted to go to Mass was to see the girls."

In his later years he had assumed the mantle of the archetypal head of the religious household.

I sat beside him in the chapel for Mass and religious ceremonies, especially the parish mission which we had every second year. He always insisted I give the priest my undivided attention in Church.

"Pay attention, otherwise it will not exist. The Consecration is concentration."

The announcement of the mission was greeted with some excitement. It became a distant second to the weather as the most important topic of conversation in the parish, "We'll never feel it til the mission" was the standard comment. Fr Allen tried to drum up some enthusiasm and spiritual fervour by describing it as "an occasion of grace." Not that grace was ever much in evidence on those days. Public enemy number one was sin. The preparation beforehand was a fastidious enterprise.

The trappings and ceremonial of services were more elaborate and formal than normal and all the component parts were done with enormous care for detail. Even the choir's attention to musical offerings of praise were better than usual, rising from the truly awful to the simply bad. That hardy perennial Soul of My Saviour was used throughout the week with reckless abandon. It was like using one's best china to feed the visitors, the family of workmen, the children at a birthday party and the dogs and cats.

Nevertheless, for most people, my grandfather included, the mission was one of the parish's great social occasions, serving as a fashion show, a community centre, a place of entertainment and two opportunities per day to meet with the locals. Some of the women wore hats. The hats in turn provoked intense discussion in the clutters of womens' gatherings outside the chapel afterwards. Their talk was inevitably fascinating for many reasons, not least of which was that delightful blend of articulate bitchery and polite, well-dressed savagery. The comments represented, in condensed form, the spontaneous venom of the parishioners, charming little darts, wicked little stabs, though sometimes not so little, which were merciless, battering some poor unfortunate, without relief or hesitation, until the conversation was abruptly halted when one of the fold was summoned to the car.

Those gatherings were no place for the meek, whatever degree of sensitivity a person had needed to be complemented by a very tough skin. Any lulls in the conversation were frequently livened up by Mary Murphy's colourful, even radiantly lyrical narratives, full of scintillating changes, sweeping moods and total disrespect for the truth. She never felt that the facts should get in the way of a good story. It would be a betrayal of her art form. This sharing of gossip and humour helped to keep the community alive, but also revealed the heartache and quiet desperation which underlined so many lives in the parish.

The sermons went on and on. When things became excessively challenging or disturbing I tried to keep my mind occupied by reciting the punchlines of my favourite television shows such as "This tape will self-destruct in five seconds" from Mission Impossible and "Book him Danno. Murder One." from Hawaii Five-O. Now and again a crying or crawling child gave a bit of diversion to the rustling and waiting congregation. For all his piety my grandfather was sceptical about the real value of the "Reds", the priests of the Redemptorist order who specialised in giving parish missions.

"They only make the pious a bit more insufferable and the sinner more despairing. Those priests are only strolling players.

There's nobody so right as the righteous. Trying to get people to change their life by ranting and raving is about as sensible as trying to cut turf with a razor blade. But sure they are the only entertainment we get in the chapel all year."

I could not understand why my grandfather could be so blasé about the whole thing. I found all the haranguing of sin and vice by the Hell-fire merchants very disconcerting. The talk was a blend of threat and fear. Those terrifying sermons lingered maddeningly with me. I found it all very confusing and very different from the pieces of the Gospel we read at school. The Jesus of the scriptures was a loving and merciful man, the milk of human kindness especially to those on the margins, a Saviour who came to call not the just but the sinners. Accusation and reprisal were the twin characteristics of the God of the preachers, not a compassionate healer but a grim reaper. Their God purified through terror. The locals had a competition about the quality of the preaching. Somebody who really excelled earned the distinction:

"He'd make the hair stand on your head."

A truly remarkable sermon merited the ultimate accolade:

"He'd make the hair stand on your head even if you were bald."

By contrast someone who was more intellectual and spoke in abstractions was dismissed in savage terms.

"He was so wishy-washy he was worse than watery tea."

Our school catechism seemed to owe more to the preachers in the Bible. We learned it by heart because we were led to believe its every word was the definitive truth. Everything was black and white. There were no grey areas. The only area for discussion was whether a particular sin was mortal or venial. The rule of thumb we learned was: "When in doubt assume it's a mortal sin." I believed everything I was told and zealously adhered to the letter of the law.

I was shocked when I was seven years old to go one of my school friends Benjy McGlynn's birthday party, one Sunday to learn that his parents had told him that he didn't have to go to Mass that day. I blurted out: "Sure that's a mortal sin to miss Mass. There will be a black mark on your soul for the rest of your life. You'll probably go to Hell."

It was an instinctive reaction. I was not trying to scare him but I could see from his haunted eyes that my words had hit home. He rushed inside to seek contrary opinion from his mother but not even her placatory words could comfort him. It was a birthday party he would not forget in a hurry. A sign of his tension was provided by his insistence that we all say grace before and after meals when we had birthday cake and minerals and later at our evening tea. Every night I would peep under my pyjamas and search for black marks on my skin which might have seeped out from under my soul.

I often thought I had not one maternal grandmother but at least ten. She was a multi-faceted personality. She was witty, kind, potentially ruthless, charming cool, patient, impatient, generous, economical, cautious, carefree, impulsive, far-seeing, enchanting, occasionally vicious, dour and charismatic. The list was endless. Her mood changed more often than the Irish weather. Her unpredictability brightened the hum-drum of family existence in which we trundled along. Her appearance was always slightly dishevelled. Her hair was never neat and she always seemed to wear clothes that were either too big or too small for her. Her face was both craggy in outline and stoically unchanging in expression. Her imposing presence belied a graceful and occasionally demure air.

As a child I was always fascinated by her eyelids. She used them like a weapon. When she lowered them a fraction she was on guard, her antennae sensing danger. The arrival of Mary Murphy normally triggered this reaction. Fireworks could be expected when she lowered them a second time as when one of her grandchildren stepped seriously out of line. There was no need for her to yell. The eyelids did the talking. They instilled fear and commanded respect. Yet when the mood was right they could signal friendships.

When my mother was out in the fields she was the captain on the bridge and we were the crew who got their rations as long as they accepted that fact. There was never any cheek. Her discipline was awe-inspiring. She was the fulcrum around which much of our childhood years revolved after my father died.

She had a caustic turn of phrase to which Mary Murphy occasionally took exception. Mary did not enjoy being on the wrong end of witheringly witty comments. Jousts between them were high drama and great entertainment value with my grandmother's eyes working overtime. Neither party played by the rules. My grandmother loved to set traps for Mary, drawing her in only to strike her with a killer punch. In truth, whenever she sat her mind to it she was a star performer and when she was on her game there was none better. She thought on her feet and with much relish kicked with her mouth. Although protocol dictated that we should keep quiet when they were in full flight we were secretly egging on my grandmother, even though the virulence of the attacks made us cringe. My grandmother did not let fly very often but when she did our kitchen was no place for the faint-hearted.

She had a memory like an elephant. Right up to my early twenties she often reminded me of two incidents from my childhood. One was when I was three years old and had left a tap running in the bathroom causing a minor flood to develop. The second occurred when I was seven and had foolishly brought my football into the hallway to practice my skills on a wet day. But a crashing sound announced that I would never be the new George Best as the football made contact with a holy water fountain.

Yet Christmas always brought out the child within her. On the morning of Christmas Eve she insisted that my grandfather would tidy up around the sides of the house in case any of the reindeers might trip over anything as Santa Claus came to deliver our presents. Not a speck of dust could be left on the side of the house in case Santy got his red coat dirty when he went up on the roof to climb down the chimney. She always insisted that the chimney-sweep was summoned to our house the day before Christmas Eve. We always had four chairs left around the Christmas tree for Santy to stack the presents individually for us. It was my grandmother who left a bottle of Guinness and a slice of Christmas cake on each chair. She decreed that each of us left a letter to Santa thanking him for the presents we got last year. There was always a handwritten note for each of us with the same message every year.

"Have a nice Christmas. Be good for your Mammy next year. Remember I will be watching you. Don't eat too many sweets on Christmas Day.

Ho, ho, ho!

Santa."

Sometimes I thought of my grandparents as the odd couple. Although born less than three miles from each other, the first time they met was in 1925 in New York. Like so many others of their generation they had been forced to go to the new world in search of something a step up from subsistence.

Before he left for America in 1922 my grandfather gave his youngest brother a one shilling piece, a small fortune for a six-year-old boy at the time. I saw that coin myself when I was nine years old. It was kept in an old matchbox and had turned jet black. At the time I could not understand why he had never spent the money. My grandfather explained how important it was to have some kind of link with the person who had emigrated. Later, in life, whenever I have heard people talking about the "power of symbols" I always associated it with that one shilling piece.

Romance sparkled between my grandparents when they worked as domestics as they brought their employers' children to St Catherine of the Holy Souls junior school. There was no time for chit-chat but they always exchanged a greeting. Finally, my grandfather plucked up the courage to ask her out. He went away above what his salary allowed and brought her to see the Athlone-born tenor, John McCormack performing in the hallowed Carnegie Hall. My grandmother was impressed by this royal treatment and enthralled by McCormack's performance.

"John McCormack was not just a singer. He was the voice."

Since my grandparents had only a small farm, their wedding breakfast took place in their home. As was the custom a bonfire blazed outside every house between the Church and our house, to wish the newly-weds well. Most of the food was home produced, and a number of barrels of drink were purchased. There had been a major fracas as the meal was being served. One of my grandaunts had raised a storm about the seating arrangements and insisted that she and her husband would be sat up at the top table.

Weddings were an unusual phenomenon in rural Ireland. They caused many a bitter feud between families but sometimes were used to heal long drawn out hostilities. Unmerciful rows were sparked off when people who thought they should have been invited to the wedding but were not vented their spleen in the most forceful way possible. Every past indiscretion or mistake, real or imagined, not only of the family in question, but of three previous generations of that family would be raked over the ashes. Inevitably a cold war broke out between the two families which might take years to resolve and sometimes was never resolved. On the other hand families who had fallen out, the most common cause of such hostilities was a failure to keep up fences on farms, might use an invitation to a wedding as a way of mending the fences in their relationship if not the actual ditches themselves.

An incident with the seating arrangements had been far too public for my grandfather's liking, but not even that had spoilt the day for him and for everyone else. There is a particular code, which applies to the description of weddings in the West of Ireland. The meaning is always hidden by the words. Rarely is the direct criticism pursued though the viciousness can be all the more striking because of that. "T'was a good job I had a feed before I left" or worse still, "If there were any mice there they would have starved with the hunger". A "great" wedding meant a good wedding. The ultimate derogatory comment was a "nice" wedding which was a disguised way of saying it was deadly boring.

For the men in particular the quality of the meal was the prime consideration. Comments like: "Ah the meal was grand" denoted dissatisfaction. The compliment that every host wanted to hear was: "Jaysus t'was a mighty feed" "Mighty" was the ultimate accolade. Anything less was failure. My grandfather glowed contentedly when he heard "mighty" recurring in a number of conversations throughout the day.

This sharing between neighbours was commonplace at the time. If you were caught short of any essential item like tea or sugar your first thought was not to make the mile and a half journey to the local shop but to ask the next door neighbour. There was no shyness about making such a request. It was part of the natural order of things.

This was important for my grandmother because she always made pounds of butter to give to our city cousins. My friends always knew that Christmas was coming when their mothers started baking Christmas cakes and puddings but my first clue that Christmas was coming was when I came home from school to see my grandmother with her sleeves rolled up to her elbows working energetically at our blue barrel butter churn.

Every Christmas my grandfather would tell the story of how of the key which unlocked his heart forever and led to his proposal of marriage. When they came back to Ireland he had travelled the three miles to give her a Christmas present because she was now his sweetheart. He arrived to find a tense situation. A full-scale row had broken out between her father and their next door neighbour on Christmas morning. Both men owned mares but they had foaled in the same field. One foal was stillborn and both mares were licking and nursing the other. My grandmother had resolved this tricky predicament by saying: "Lead the foal into the stream down at the end of the field and the real mother will follow it in." Her ruse worked and to her father's delight it was his horse which waded into the cold stream without hesitation.

My grandfather knew a wise head when he saw one. This was the woman for him. Their love was like the Victoria Falls. It went on and on, though never softly.

Six
Set Free For Freedom

IN Rome there was once a poor slave whose name was Maximus. His master was a cruel man, and so unkind to him that at last Maximus ran away. Night had fallen, bringing with it a drenching drizzle that seeped through cloaks and trickled down the backs of necks. It was miserable weather and Maximus wished he had a home of his own and that he was sitting in front of a blazing fire.

He hid himself in caves for days. One time he was sleeping when he was woken by a great noise. It was another murky day, with leaden skies filled with fast-moving clouds, and only the faintest hint of sun glimmering in the east. It had been a wet night, and the streets were clogged with rain-thinned horse manure. A lion had come into the cave, and was roaring loudly. Maximus was very much afraid, for he felt certain that the beast would kill him. A sheen of sweat appeared on his forehead and speckled the skin above his lips. Soon, however, he saw that lion was not angry, but that he limped as though his foot hurt him.

Then Maximus grew so bold that he took hold of the lion's lame paw to see what was the matter. The lion stood quite still, and rubbed his head against the man's shoulder. He seemed to say, 'I know that you will help me.'

Maximus lifted the paw from the ground, and saw that it was a long, sharp thorn which hurt the lion so much. He took the end of the thorn in his fingers; then he have a strong, quick pull, and out it came. The lion was full of joy. He jumped about like a dog, and licked his hands and feet of his new friend.

Maximus was not at all afraid after this. And when night came, he and the lion lay down and slept side by side. For a long time, the lion brought food to Maximus every day, and the two became such good friends that Maximus had a wonderful time. He knew things were too good to be true. And then something terrible happened.

One day some soldiers were passing and spotted Maximus. They captured him and brought him back to Rome. It was the law at the time that every slave who ran away from his master should be made to fight a hungry lion. Although they were pagans the Romans celebrated Christmas Day except they did so in a cruel way. They went to the Coliseum to see some poor Christians thrown to the mercy of fierce lions. So a ferocious lion was shut for a while without food, and a time was set for the fight.

When Christmas Day came, thousands of people crowded to see the sport. The rain clouds that had been dogging Rome for weeks were blown away by a cool, fresh wind from the south. The morning dawned with a blaze of gold when the sun made a rare appearance, and the sky was clear and perfect blue. There was an atmosphere of happy anticipation from the festival itself and the feast that had been arranged for that evening.

Every spectator seemed to have made an effort with their appearance, and even the most exacting standards of sartorial elegance were surpassed by some of the crowd. Nobody had ever seen so many polished shoes and brushed cloaks. The sun blazed through, casting pools of coloured light into the stadium, and slaves had decorated it with flowers of primrose and blue, so that the whole building was infused with the sweet scent of them. The choir excelled themselves with an anthem they had been practicing for weeks.

The door opened, and poor Maximus was brought in. He was almost dead with fear, for the roars of the lion were ringing in his ears.

Then the hungry lion rushed in. For such a bulky creature, he had an uncannily light thread, like a large predator. With a single leap he reached the slave. Maximus gave a great cry, not out of fear, but of gladness. It was his old friend, the lion of the cave.

The people, who had expected to see the man killed by the lion, were filled with wonder. They saw Maximus put his arms around the lion's neck; they saw the lion down at his feet, and lick them lovingly; they saw the great beast rub his head against the slave's face as though he wanted to be petted. They could not understand what it all meant.

They asked Maximus to tell them about it. So he stood up before them, and, with his arm around the lion's neck, told how he and the beast had lived together in the cave.

When he had finished everyone was in tears. They clapped and shouted, 'Let this man go free. Let this man go free.'

Others cried, 'Let the lion free too. Let them both go free.'

For behold, from this day on all generations shall call me blessed. For he who is mighty has done great things for me, and holy is his name. And his mercy is on those who worship him from here to the last day. Behold, I am the handmaid of the Lord; let it be to me according to your word

Seven

The Three Wise Men

NOW the birth of Jesus Christ took place in the following way. In the sixth month the angel Gabriel was sent from God to a city of Galilee named Nazareth, to a virgin and her name was Mary. And he came to her and said, 'Hail, O favoured one, the Lord is with you!' But she was greatly troubled at the saying, and considered in her mind what sort of greeting this might be. And the angel said to her, 'Do not be afraid, Mary, for you have found favour with God. And behold, you will conceive in your womb and bear a son, and you shall call his name Jesus. He will be great, and will be called the Son of the Most High; And the Lord God will give to him the throne of his father David, and he will reign over the house of Jacob for ever; and of his kingdom there will be no end.'

And Mary said to the angel, 'How shall this be, since I have no husband?' And the angel said to her, 'The Holy Spirit will come upon you, and the power of the Most High will overshadow you; therefore the child to be born will be called holy the Son of God. Blessed art thou among women and blessed is the fruit of your womb.'

And Mary said, 'My soul magnifies the Lord, and my spirit rejoices in God my Saviour, for he has regarded the low estate of his handmaiden. For behold, from this day on all generations shall call me blessed. For he who is mighty has done great things for me, and holy is his name. And his mercy is on those who worship him from here to the last day. Behold, I am the handmaid of the Lord; let it be to me according to your word.'

Mary was betrothed to Joseph, before they came together she was found to be child of the Holy Spirit, and her husband Joseph, being an honourable man and unwilling to put her to shame, decided to divorce her quietly. But as he considered this, behold, an angel of the Lord appeared to him in a dream, saying, 'Joseph, son of David, do not dare not to take Mary your wife, for what which is conceived in her is of the Holy Spirit; she will bear a son, and you shall call his name Jesus, for he will save his people from their sins'. When Joseph woke from his sleep, he did as the angel of the Lord commanded him; he took his wife, but knew her not until she had borne him a child.

In those days a decree went out from Caesar Augustus that all the world should be enrolled. And all went to be enrolled each to their own city. And Joseph also went up from Galilee, to the city of David, which is called Bethlehem with Mary who was with child. And while they were there, the time came for her to be delivered. And she gave birth to her first-born son and wrapped him in swaddling cloths, and laid him in a manger, because there was no place for them in the inn. So farmer John gave them the use of his stable.

And in that region there were shepherds out in the field, keeping watch over their flock by night. And an angel of the Lord appeared to them, and the glory of the Lord, shone around them, and they were filled with fear. And the angel said to them, 'Be not afraid; for behold, I bring you good news of a great joy which will come to all the people; for to you is born this day in the city of David a Saviour, who is Christ the Lord. And this will be a sign for you: you will find a babe wrapped in swaddling cloths and in a manger. And suddenly there was with the angel a multitude of the heavenly host praising God and saying, 'Glory to God in the highest and on earth peace among men with whom he is pleased.'

When the angels went away from them into heaven, the shepherds said to one another, 'Let us go over to Bethlehem and see this thing that has happened, which the Lord has made known to us.' And they went with haste, and found Mary and Joseph, and the babe lying in a manger. And when they saw it they made known the saying which had been told them concerning this child; and all who heard it wondered at what the shepherds told them. But Mary kept all these things, pondering them in her heart. And the shepherds returned, glorifying and praising God for all they had heard and seen, as it had been told them.

In Bethlehem of Judea in the days of the Herod the king, behold three wise men from the East came to Jerusalem, arrived saying, 'Where is he who has been born king of the Jews? For we have seen his star in the East, and have come to worship him.' And behold their names were: Tom, Dick and Harry.

When Herod, the king heard this he was troubled, and all Jerusalem with him; and assembling all the chief priests and scribes of the people, he inquired of them where the Christ was to be born. They told him, 'In Bethlehem of Judea; for so it is written by the prophet:

'And you, O Bethlehem, in the land of Judah,
Are by no means least among the rulers of Judah;
For from you shall come a ruler
Who will govern my people Israel.'

Then Herod summoned the wise men secretly and ascertained from them what time the star appeared; and he sent them to Bethlehem, saying, 'Go and search diligently for the child, and when you have found him bring me the word, that I too may come to worship him.'

When they had heard the king they went on their way; and lo, the star which they had seen in the East went before them, till it came to rest over the place where the child was. When they saw the star they rejoiced exceedingly with great joy; and going into the stable they saw the child with Mary and his mother.

Then their joy quickly gave way to horror for they were brilliant bureaucrats.

And behold Tom said: 'This stable is in convention of Clause 37, subsection 246 of the Health and safety Act. Farmer John must be punished severely.'

And behold Dick said: 'Having animals and a baby in the one residence is a serious violation of Section 89, Clause 432, paragraph 6785 of the Hygiene Act. Somebody must be held to account.'

And behold Harry said in a solemn voice: 'This a flagrant breach of Section 9076, Clause 4367, paragraph 9087 of the Child Care Act. Mary and Joseph are clearly not fit parents and this baby must be taken from them on a permanent basis and brought under the jurisdiction of the appropriate authorities.'

Tom, Dick and Harry immediately transported Jesus on the back of a camel to the Office of Circumlocution where an emergency hearing was held. 46 lawyers and 72 bureaucrats gave their expert opinions and after three days it was decreed that Joseph and Mary should be prosecuted for child abuse and would receive the maximum sentence of seven years in prison and that Jesus should be put in a foster home for children at risk.

When the case was reported in the media there was horror. Doe Juffy, the man with the ears of the nation form his 'Camelline' soapbox was inundated with messages from people seething with moral indignation about the recklessness of the family.

Tom, Dick and Harry became national heroes. Tom was made Head of the Holy Land Health Services Executive. Dick became Minister of Health. Harry went on to become Health Correspondent with The Jerusalem Times.

Farmer John had to pay such a crippling fine that he had to sell his farm and spent the rest of his life in poverty.

Mary and Joseph never saw Jesus again.

All three lived unhappily ever after.

Eight
William's Wisdom
and Witness

LONG ago there lived a poor woodcutter named William. Every day he went by the river to the forest with his strong, sharp axe over his shoulder. He was able to buy just enough food for his family by cutting wood.

On his way to the forest shallow bogs lined the sides of the track, and stunted elder and aspen trees hunched over them, as if attempting to shrink away from the icy winds that often howled in from the flat expanses to the north and east. He had been told that the wind that shrieked across the hills with such violence every winter came from icy kingdoms above Norway and Sweden, where the land was perpetually frozen and the rays of sun never reached. Reeds and rushes waved and hissed back and forth, and the grey sky that stretched above always seemed much larger here than it did elsewhere. As they walked, more briskly than usual because it was cold, ducks flapped in sudden agitation in the undergrowth, and then flew away with piercing cackles.

The other early risers looked cold and miserable as they trudged along, and seemed to be wearing clothes that had dulled to a shade of drab brown in the wet semi-darkness. Even the cows that were being herded for milking were dirty and bedraggled.

Poor William was sad on Christmas Eve because he had enough to buy bread for his family but had no money to buy a turkey or potatoes or ham for the dinner or toys for his seven children or even a small present for his beautiful and kind wife Winnie.

Then just when he thought his spirits could go no lower disaster struck. The path by the river was very icy and William slipped and his axe fell into the river.

'What will I do?' the woodcutter cried. 'I've lost my axe! How will I feed my children now?'

Just as he finished spoke, up from the lake rose a beautiful lady. She was the water queen of the river, and came to the surface when she heard his sad voice. 'What is your problem?' she asked in a soft, gentle voice. The woodman told her about his situation, and at once she sank beneath the surface, and reappeared in a moment with an axe made of silver.

'Is this your axe?' she asked.

The woodcutter shook his head sadly as he thought of all the things he could buy for his children with such an axe. But the axe was not his, so he shook his head, and answered, 'My axe was only made of steel.'

The water queen lay the silver axe on the bank, and sank into the river again. In a moment she rose and showed the woodman another axe. 'Maybe this one is yours?' she asked.

The woodcutter replied, 'Oh, no!' he replied. 'This one is made of gold. It's much, much more valuable than mine.'

The water queen lay the golden axe on the bank. Once again she sank. Up she rose. This time she held the missing axe.

'Ah, yes. That one is mine.' the woodcutter said.

'It is yours.' said the water queen, 'and so are these other two now. They are gifts from the river, because you have told the truth.' And that evening William walked home with all three axes on his shoulder, happy thinking of all the good things he could now buy for his family even though the day had grown even darker since they had been in the lake, and black clouds slouched above, moving quickly in the rising wind. Rain fell in a persistent, heavy drizzle that quickly soaked through his cloak and boots. He was soon shivering. It was much too cold to travel at the ambling pace he usually favoured.

His house was a tiny cottage with a red-tiled roof and ivy-clad walls. Smoke curled from its chimney, to be whisked away quickly by the wind. From the house next door came the sweet, warm scent of newly baked bread. When he arrived at his front door, and had made his way through the dripping vegetation, he was puffing and panting like a pair of bellows, although it had still not being fast enough to drive the chill from his bones. Shivering, but with a sense of triumph, he knocked on the door. The bright blue eyes of his wife peered out at him. Before he could announce his news, the door had been fully opened, and his children nearly crushed him with their loving embraces.

The following morning, just as the first glimmerings of dawn lightened the sky, he dragged himself from a deep sleep, and washed and shaved in the dim light, muttering under his breath when he could not find a clean shirt. The light danced across the thin green grass in tiny pools of brightness as it filtered through branches that were shorn of their leaves. The village was unusually peaceful.

When his family woke they could not believe their eyes because William had a wonderful Christmas feast prepared for them, toys for all the children and a beautiful brooch for Winnie. Seeing the joy and surprise on their faces, tears filled his eyes. He gave them a surreptitious scrub with the back of his hand.

Later that night when the kids were sleeping soundly Winnie asked William what he had learned from his Christmas adventure. He thought for a long while before answering: 'Our life is a book of chapters three: the past, the present, and the yet-to-be. The past is gone, it is stowed away; the present we live with every day; the future is not for us to see, it is locked away and God holds the key.'

There were peasants wearing undyed homespun tunics and there were merchants in clothes of many colours with fashionable shoes. Among them was a small, bustling character wearing a brand new cloak

Nine

Walk The Talk

A NEW priest in a small parish spent the first few months of his ministry calling on his parishioners to be actively involved in the parish. But they would hardly turn up to any of his services. He began to feel oppressed by the great emptiness. Desperate, one day after seeing one barefoot, ragged woman who was sobbing bitterly, he placed a notice in the local newspaper stating that as the parish was dead, it was his duty to give it a decent burial.

The funeral would be held on Christmas Day. On the morning the priest was admiring the impressive carvings around the great door in the west front, when a crash preceded a string of people traipsing in. The air rang with noise, frightening two pigeons that had been roosting among the rafters; the sounds of their agitated flapping, and the shrieks of a wistful woman as one flew too close to her added to the general sense of hustle and bustle. The men, who had been talking quietly outside the Church, began to speak more loudly in order to make themselves heard. The more salacious the gossip the more it was relished like the man said to engage in unnatural acts with animals or the women alleged to practice satanic rites in the churchyard after dark.

Very curious, the whole parish had turned out. Some were rubbing sleep from their eyes, clearly having just dragged themselves from their beds, while a few farmers had hands that were stained dark from a lifelong struggle with the peaty brownness of the local soil. There were peasants wearing undyed homespun tunics and there were merchants in clothes of many colours with fashionable shoes. Among them was a small, bustling character wearing a brand new cloak. He had dark, greasy hair that was worn too long, and eyes so close together that the priest wondered whether either could see anything other than his nose. He strode purposefully towards the front seat and looked at the priest up and down, as he might imagine a horse he considered buying.

The pale spring sun that had cheered the village at dawn had long since slipped behind a bank of dense clouds, and a bitter wind had picked up. Now long before noon fell, it promised to be a miserable night, with wind and rain in the offing.

At the front of the church, the Congregation saw a high coffin smothered in flowers. The preacher carried out his funeral rites in the usual way and preached a homily; then he invited his congregation to step forward and pay their last respects to the dearly beloved who had departed.

The long line filed by. Each mourner peeped into the coffin and turned away with a guilty, sheepish look for in the coffin, titled at the correct angle was a large mirror. Everyone saw themselves.

Ten

A Wise Woman

EVERYONE in the town gathered for a big meeting in the town square on Christmas Day. People were very angry because it seemed that the Christmas spirit was gone forever. There was so much cruelty in the town and everyone seemed to have forgotten how to be good, kind, generous, honest and helpful. The meeting went on for hours and hours because everyone was blaming everyone else for all their problems. Eventually someone suggested, 'Why not ask the Wise Woman of the Woods what we should do?' It was agreed that the oldest man in the town should go and speak to her. In the heavy rain water dripped from his face, drenching the fringe of grey hair that poked out from under his hood and trickling down the sides of his face. He found the Wise Woman of the Woods and explained why everyone in the town was so unhappy and not getting on with each other.

She was a short, dour-faced specimen in her early sixties. Her clothes were made of the finest cloth, but she clearly allowed none of the latest fashions to influence her. Her voluminous skirts were gathered uncomfortably under her large bosom, and were rather too short, so that a pair of stout calves poked from under them. Her tunic was decorated with more buttons than anyone in the town had ever seen on a single garment. Her handsome shoes were made from soft calfskin, and the jewellery that glittered at her throat and on her fingers were exquisite.

There was a determined look in her pale green eyes, and the strength of her character was evident in the way her chin jutted out in front of her. She was followed not by ladies in waiting, but by a manservant.

She was an honest, uncomplicated soul, and expected others

to be the same. Her open nature was one of the things that people loved about her, because it was not something many found in the town, where people seemed to have been trained to prevaricate.

The old man asked her what they should do. She said, 'You must all open your eyes.'

The man was shocked and puzzled so he asked, 'What do you mean by that?'

The Wise Woman of the Woods replied, 'One of the people living in your town is the Chosen One in disguise and you are blind to this.'

As the old man went back to the town his heart beat fast at the thought that the Chosen One was right there in their town. How is it they had all failed to recognize him or was it a her? And who could it be? The Fireman? The Hairdresser? The policewoman? The bank manager? No, not he; he had too many bad sides to him. But then the Wise Woman of the Woods had said the Chosen One was in disguise. Could those bad sides be the disguise? Come to think of it, everyone in the town had bad sides. And one of them had to be the Chosen One!

The men were tall and strong, while their womenfolk gave the impression that they could wrestle with cows, toss haystacks over their shoulders, and tear down big trees with their bare hands. Even the children seemed physically powerful. But then there was David, the man who always cowered behind others because he was such a puny specimen. His complexion was pallid and unhealthy, and his hair fell in oily tendrils around his shoulders. Unlike many, his clothes were well-made and expensive. He was generally clad in a handsome blue coat with silver buttons on the sleeves, and his trousers were bright orange and appeared to be made out of silk. At least it could not possibly be him? But then maybe he was exactly the sort of person who could be the Chosen One?

When the old man got back to the town he called everyone together one more time and told them what he had discovered.

They looked at one another in disbelief. The Chosen One? Here? Incredible! But here in disguise. So, maybe. What if it was so-and-so? Or the other one over there? Or even . . .

One thing was certain: if the Chosen One was there in disguise it was not likely that they would recognize her or him. So they started to treat everyone with respect and kindness. 'You never know,' they said to themselves when they dealt with one another, 'maybe this is the one.'

On his wrist sat his favourite hawk. As he turned for home he felt very thirsty because his Christmas lunch had been very salty. His pet hawk had flown away but his master wasn't worried because he knew it could make its own way home

Eleven
Don't Look Back In Anger

ONCE there was a famous hero and warrior. There was never a braver man in all the world.

He had a mop of red-brown that was worn overly long. A smattering of freckles across the bridge of his nose gave him a curiously adolescent appearance, and his grubby fingers had nails that had been chewed almost to the quick. He had a pleasant face and a mouth that always looked ready for laughter.

One Christmas Day to relax after all his battles he went walking in the country. Not for the first time he mused that while clear skies were very pretty, they heralded a cold night, and already he could feel a frost beginning to form on the ground underfoot.

On his wrist sat his favourite hawk. As he turned for home he felt very thirsty because his Christmas lunch had been very salty. His pet hawk had flown away but his master wasn't worried because he knew it could make its own way home.

He knew there was a spring somewhere nearby. He went in search of it and first found its stream. The water looked cool and inviting. He shed his leggings to wade across it so that he could examine both banks simultaneously. He enjoyed the sensation of cold water on his skin, and allowed his powerful, white feet to dabble on the water's edge. He removed his shirt and waded into the shallows to dive into the cool blackness of the deeper water.

At last he saw some water trickling down over the edge of the rock. He knew there was a spring farther up.

The warrior took a little silver cup from his pocket. He held it so as to catch the slowly falling drops.

It took a long time to fill the cup; and the king was so thirsty that he could hardly wait. At last it was nearly full. He put the cup to his lips, and was about to drink.

Suddenly there was a whirring sound in the air, and the cup was knocked from his hands. The water was all spilled upon the ground.

The great hero looked up to see who had done this thing. It was his pet hawk. He could feel the anger begin to boil inside him.

The great warrior picked up the cup, and again held it to catch the trickling drops. When the cup was half full, he lifted it toward his mouth. But before it had touched his lips, the hawk swooped down again, and knocked it from his hands.

By now the great warrior was very, very angry. He filled his cup a third time but before he tried to drink, he drew his sword, fury erupting.

'Now, my former friend, beware. You wouldn't do this to me again and live.'

He had barely finished speaking before the hawk swooped down and knocked the cup from his hand. But the great warrior was ready and struck the bird as it passed. The hawk fell and lay dying on the ground.

The great hero went looking for his cup only to discover that it had fallen down behind the rocks where he could reach it. He had no choice but to climb up to the source of the spring. It was a tough climb but at last he reached his destination. There indeed was a pool of water; but what was there in the pool, and almost filling it? It was a huge, dead snake full of poison.

The warrior let out a great scream. 'That poor hawk saved my life. But how did I repay him? He was my best friend, and I have killed him.'

He climbed back down and took up the dying bird in is arms and whispered softly to him until the hawk was dead. Tears fell from the great hero's eyes like a raging river. As the tears dried up his face became suffused with rage again.

He was still sobbing softly when he got home late that Christmas night, brushing a speck of blood from his elegant cloak, held together by a gold brooch in an elegant fold over his shoulder. His wife mulled some wine, and they sat next to the roaring fire, listening to the wind rattle the window shutters. The wood released the scent of pine as it burned, combining pleasantly with the aroma of the cloves and ginger that were tied in small bags around the house – a frequent precaution against winter fevers. Sensing his pain his wife asked, 'What's wrong?'

The great warrior replied, 'Is it every okay to act in anger?'

So Truth promised and agreed to go along with Falsehood for a while, not because he liked his company so much, but because he was so hungry he thought he would faint soon if he didn't get something into his stomach

Twelve

The Christmas Truth

ONE Christmas, Truth decided that it was time to end his hostility to Falsehood so they met each other on the road.

'Good afternoon,' said Truth.

'Good afternoon,' replied Falsehood his face alight with pleasure. 'And how are you doing these days?'

'Not very well at all, I'm afraid,' sighed Truth. 'The times are tough for a fellow like me, you know.'

'Yes, I can see that,' said Falsehood, glancing up and down at Truth's ragged clothes. 'You look like you haven't had anything to eat for ages.'

'To be honest, I haven't,' said Truth. 'No one seems to want to employ me these days. Wherever I go, most people ignore me or mock me. It's getting discouraging. I'm beginning to ask myself, why I do it.'

'And why the devil do you? Come with me, and I'll show you how to get along. There's no reason in the world why you can't stuff yourself with as much as you want to eat, like me, and dress in the finest clothes, like me this Christmas. But you must promise not to say a word against me while we're together.'

So Truth promised and agreed to go along with Falsehood for a while, not because he liked his company so much, but because he was so hungry he thought he would faint soon if he didn't get something into his stomach. They walked down the road until they came to a city, and Falsehood at once led the way to the very best table at the restaurant.

'Waiter, bring us your best food and your finest wine.' All afternoon they ate and drank the most magnificent Christmas dinner that Truth had ever experiences. At last, when they could hold no more, Falsehood began banging his fist on the table and calling for the manager, who came running at once.

The manager was a sturdy man in his fifties, who was burned a deep nut-brown by the sun. His forearms were sinewy and knotted, indicating that the large garden they had passed on their way in, with its neat rows of vegetables and herbs, was probably tended by him personally and that he was no stranger to hard work. He had twinkling blue eyes, wiry grey hair and a large gap between two of his teeth. Truth sensed he was adept at preventing arguments among his customers.

'What the devil kind of place is this?' Falsehood snapped, 'I gave that waiter a gold piece nearly an hour ago, and he still hasn't brought our change.'

The manager summoned the waiter, who said he had never even seen a penny out of the gentleman.

'What?' Falsehood shouted, so that everyone in the place turned and looked. 'I can't believe this place! Innocent, law-abiding citizens come into eat on this most special of days, and you rob them of their hard-earned cash. You're a gang of thieves and liars. You may have fooled me once, but you'll never see me again. Here.' He threw a gold piece at the manager. 'Now this time bring me my change.'

But the manager, fearing his restaurant's reputation would suffer, refused to take the gold piece, and instead brought Falsehood change for the first gold piece he claimed to have spent. Then he took the waiter aside and looked at him up and down as he might a pile of dung and called him a thief, and said that he was going to fire him. And as much as the waiter protested that he had never collected a cent from the man, the manager refused to believe him.

'Oh Truth, where have you hidden yourself?' the waiter sighed. 'Have you now deserted even us hard-working souls?'

'No, I'm here,' Truth groaned to himself, 'But my judgment gave way to my hunger, and now I can't speak up without breaking my promise to Falsehood.'

As soon as they were on the street, Falsehood gave a great laugh and slapped Truth on the back. 'You see how the world works?' he cried. 'I managed it all quite well, don't you think?'

When Monica answered the door she looked absolutely frantic and she quickly led Reverend Thomas into the kitchen. 'Is your father upstairs?' 'My father died forty years ago. I wanted you for Dad.'

Thirteen

All Creatures
Meek and Tall

'I DON'T believe it', muttered Reverend Thomas as the shrill ringing of the phone woke him from his deep slumber. He turned on the light and saw that it was three a.m. He was just a half an hour in bed. Cleaning up the Church after Midnight Service had taken longer than normal.

From afar he gave the impression of frailty, and his voice was barely audible in the massive vaults of the Church. But on closer inspection, he was not frail at all. He was a slight man in his mid-fifties with a head of thick, greying hair and that came from clambering over scaffolding and supervising the building work he always seemed to be engaged in.

With his eyes still sleep-leaden Reverend Thomas answered the phone. 'Hello', he said tentatively. Immediately he pulled the phone back from his ear because of the sound of a woman wailing loudly. Eventually the crying subsided enough for him to hear, 'Reverend Thomas. Its Monica Waring here? Can you come quickly? It's Dad. He's just going to die.'

Reverend Thomas heard himself say, 'I'll be there in 10 minutes.' but he was shocked. Monica was 78. He would have sworn her father died years ago.

When Monica answered the door she looked absolutely frantic and she quickly led Reverend Thomas into the kitchen.

'Is your father upstairs?'

'My father died forty years ago. I wanted you for Dad.'

'I'm sorry Monica I don't understand', replied the puzzled minister.

Then the woman pointed to a big basket beside the fire where an old cat was wheezing and coughing frighteningly. Through her sobs she said, "That cat has been my only friend for the last 17 years. I call him Dad because he always sits . . . sat on that chair under the television where my father used to sit.'

Reverend Thomas gave the cat a blessing. He stayed on until 7.30 when the cat died and as he took Dad away to arrange to have him buried Monica looked as if her heart was broken.

The following day broke bright and clear, with the sun soaring into the sky and flooding the Church with light for morning Mass. Reverend Thomas was haunted by the memory of Monica's sad eyes as he prayed alone in the Church. St Paul's did not boast much stained glass, but it had a little, and light pooled in occasional multicoloured splatters on the nave floor.

One thing he had always been good at was losing himself in his mind. For him his brain was a very interesting place to be lost. He could entertain himself endlessly with memories of moments and mischief. That evening the minister got a brainwave. He drove to visit a parishioner who was home from jail for Christmas. Although he was often in trouble Reverend Thomas knew that Clive was at heart a good man. All his problems were caused by drinking.

Reverend Thomas smiled as he said, 'I need you to do me a favour Clive.'

'You have been very good to down the years Reverend. Anything I can.'

'What I want you to do is to give up your cat Millie. I know you're very fond of her but you can't look after her properly in jail. I've got a good home for her.'

Clive nodded 'You're right. Take her. She deserves better than me. She's the friendliest cat in Ireland.'

20 minutes later Reverend Thomas walked in alone to discover

Monica sitting by the fire. Her eyes were red. The minister said, 'I need a big favour. I want you to look after a friend of mine.'

As Monica started to protest, Reverend Thomas whistled. Millie raced in and went straight up to Monica and started licking her face. The woman started crying but his time her tears were of joy.

*The jockeys appeared
from the weighing room,
bringing a burst of colour
to the scene. The crowd watched
as the jockeys mounted, their
silks shining brightly*

Fourteen
An Error of Judgement

ONE of the big events in Ireland every Christmas is the horse racing meeting at Leopardstown when the people of Ireland came in their thousands to have a flutter at the races, the women in particular dressing in their best outrageous hats for the occasion.

There was a strong security presence. There was still plenty of racing folklore surrounding a sabotage attempt at a racecourse where a heating boiler nearly blew up after someone had inserted a dead mouse as plug into a pipe of the safety system.

One year Frank the farmer went to the racing on Saint Stephen's Day. Everyone was in thick, heavy overcoats with gloves, scarves and warm hats that generally gave people a little respite from the inclement weather. The coats sometimes covered the most ghastly Christmas jumpers but the odd hilarious one too.

Frank's nervousness was clearly visible as he shifted his weight from foot to foot, unable to remain still for more than a few seconds. The jockeys appeared from the weighing room, bringing a burst of colour to the scene. The crowd watched as the jockeys mounted their silks shining brightly.

Frank the farmer had brought 500 hundred euro with him to bet on the horses. He decided that he would not put a bet on the first race. The horses circled, forming themselves into race-card order for the traditional parade in front of the stands. Another turn around the parade ring and then they were filing out. Then the horses broke from the formal parade, their jockeys turning them to canter down to have a look at the first fence while the crowd took a collective breath in preparation for the race itself. Last minute instructions were clearly being passed on by the owners to their trainers.

As Frank the farmer watched the horses get ready for the races he noticed that there was a priest in the parade ring and he blessed one of the horses called 'The Christmas Presence' on his head with some holy water. The horse won the race by half a mile and at a price of fifty-to-one! Many in the crowd cheered and jumped up and down with excitement, slapping one another on his back, not least to try to keep themselves warm against an icy wind that was blowing straight into their faces.

Frank smiled at the owner's ruddy-faced image shown on the big television screen, his huge grin stretching almost from one side of the screen to the other. It was such moments that were essential to the success and popularity of jump racing. The fact that a small shopkeeper from Leitrim could do it and gave others hope that they too might own the winner of a great race. The anticipation of such a victory kept many racehorse owners paying out hefty training fees for years in its pursuit.

Frank the farmer decided not to bet on the second race until he would check if the priest would give another blessing this time. Sure enough the priest blessed one of the horses called 'The Christmas Miracle' on the head with holy water. This time the horse won by a full mile. Frank's adrenalin was climbing to stratospheric levels.

Frank the farmer was very impressed and decided to follow the priest before the third race. He walked past a long line of food outlets, each doing a roaring trade with a choice of roast-pork baps, fish and chips, meat pies, assorted delicacies, Asian noodles or huge slices of pepperoni pizza. As he walked there was a distinct unevenness to his gait. He spoke to no one of interest and interacted only with the man behind the counter at one of the food stalls where he bought a large Cornish pastry that he proceeded to inject with copious amounts of tomato ketchup from a pump.

Before the third race Frank saw the priest blessing a horse

called Benedictus. The horse won at a canter at 100 to one. Afterwards he thought the bookmaker was speaking Latin when he wryly: 'Jesus Benedictus wrecked us.'

Frank bought a toasted ham sandwich. As he ate he watched a leading jockey laughing and joking with a group of admiring ladies, all of them protected from the biting wind by thick fur coats and hats.

After his snack Frank stood in the line of expectant clusters, many of them no doubt dreaming of winning the 'big one'. The excitement of the crowd was palpable.

This time he saw the priest blessing a horse called 'The Christmas Treasure' with holy water except this time he did not just bless the horse on the head but on his back, his four legs and his tail as well. Frank the farmer was certain that with such a blessing The Christmas Treasure was sure to win the race so he bet the full five hundred euro on the horse.

Frank the farmer had a big smile on his face on his chubby cheeks as he watched the race starting with his light brown eyes because The Christmas Treasure took off like a train and he had a big lead. His heart was beating quickly and he could ever hear the rush of blood in his ears above the sound of the crowd. With each second he became more and more anxious.

Then disaster.

The Christmas Treasure fell at the first fence.

A few minutes later the horse breathed his last breath. At that moment the scuttling clouds spilled open and delivered still more rain to the area.

Frank the farmer was sad and upset. He raced straight up to the priest and said: 'I don't understand. You gave a small blessing to the first three horses and they won their races easily. You gave a big blessing to the fourth horse and he fell and died. How could that happen?'

The priest shook his head and put his hand on Frank's shoulder and softly said: 'Ah, you poor man. You don't understand the difference between a blessing and the last rites.'

Fifteen
Fiona's Doll

IT is often said that it is in giving that we receive. Yet few people are comfortable receiving. Often when we say: 'You shouldn't have' that is what we mean. We do not want to feel a sense of obligation to people. In this way we deprive others of the opportunity to experience the joy of giving.

Fiona Finneran was a young girl from the West of Ireland, Roscommon to be more specific. One day her father was driving her home from school when they were run into by a drunken driver. As the two burly ambulance-men took her gently up the steps of the ambulance they noticed her badly scarred doll covered in a sea of broken glass. Although Fiona was unconscious one of them put the doll by her side. The doll accompanied her right through to the operating table.

Over the next few weeks Fiona was in intensive care, clinging on to life by her fingertips. Gradually Fiona started to recover her senses and her strength. Her recovery was greatly accelerated by the untiring efforts of her kindly surgeon, Dr Frank Walsh. He was a man of immense self-confidence, used to getting his own way, and someone not to argue with unless you wanted to lose. He was in his early sixties, with longish salt-and-pepper hair and beard. He was as tall as Fiona's brothers Liam and James, but leaner, though his arms and shoulders, bulged with muscles from hours in the gym. He was far stronger than most men half his age and tougher than anyone Fiona had ever met. Born in New York he had spent 20 years in the military and fought in Vietnam and done some things that he never talked about. He would simply say that war was Darwinism at its most efficient and most ruthless. On the right side of his face near his jaw was the shining seam of a scar.

He was not much affected by criticism. He also joked that he wore two vests when people were unhappy with him. He then took the heat out of the situation when they asked in bewilderment what he meant. He dutifully explained that King Charles the First wore two vests at his execution so the crowds would not see him shiver from cold and assume he was afraid of death. He then went on to remind them of an Afghan tribal leader who had asked his bodyguard if they could prevent him from being killed. 'No', they had replied 'but be comforted by the knowledge that we will be there to kill the assassin.'

Throughout her long convalescence Fiona's doll was a constant companion.

After three months the time came for Fiona to return home on Christmas Eve. Outside the watery snow began, tentatively at first, a slow, uneven falling of fat drops. Dr Walsh called in to say goodbye. Her face lit up when she saw her hero, and her gait was suddenly more sprightly. With unexpected grace for a man so large the doctor effected an elegant bow. Impressed by his gracious manners, Fiona stepped forward to return the greeting.

She gave him a grin with her perfect white teeth, and her brilliant blue eyes sparkled with pleasure. At first she laughed, a pleasant, sweet sound that was a welcome change for the doctor after the misery and pain he had witnessed that night when one of his difficult operations had not been successful.

Then tears toppled in steady streams down her cheeks when Fiona said: 'Dr Walsh, I want to thank you for helping me. I have a small Christmas gift for you.' She handed him the battered doll. He shook his head slightly and his mouth twitched. This was as close as the stoic surgeon ever came to strong emotion. The marvellous medic took it home with him that evening without any qualms.

The following day as the sky was heavy and grey, a fine snow beginning again, like ashes from a fire he had it put in a glass case in his office. He rubbed his hands vigorously as he mumbled to nobody but his shadow that he paid a small fortune for heat but could still feel his breath in the morning.

Frequently visitors to his office asked him about it. He told them Fiona's story and explained that of all the honours heaped upon him in the course of his illustrious career this was the one that meant the most to him. Some people wondered if he might not have been better off letting Fiona keep the doll.

'Why should I deny her the joy of giving?' was his reply.

In the midst of the crop of Christmas classics she was startled to hear a version of a song she had heard in years which returned to her like an old friend. It was the distinctive voice of Joe Dolan singing 'O Holy Night'

Sixteen

From Darkness to Light

AT the top of Grafton Street a group of tuneless singers make up a raucous street choir, managing to turn the timeless classic Silent Night into a contradiction in terms. As they are trying to raise money for charity and it is the season of goodwill to all men and women Susan felt obliged to give them a donation. Some of the men singing look as out of place as a nun in a brothel.

Scurrying shoppers like ants at a party, arms laden with gift-wrapped Christmas presents head home as the Dublin dusk descends. A little girl is mesmerised by Switzers' window with its glorious gnomes, who move majestically to the rhythm of the music. Crowds gather, young and old, just to savour the innocence of it all.

After picking up her last Christmas presents Susan called into her friend, John Fitzgerald Montini Byrne, on the way home. As it was the season of goodwill she won't dwell on how untidy his flat was – suffice to say she had to wipe her shoes after leaving it. The Christmas Spirit is sadly lacking in the antics of the drivers in the "rush hour" traffic. As always the car radio brought a crumb of comfort to her frayed nerves. In the midst of the crop of Christmas classics she was startled to hear a version of a song she had heard in years which returned to her like an old friend. It was the distinctive voice of Joe Dolan singing O Holy Night. Suddenly she became entangled in the clinging cobwebs of childhood. She became a seven year old girl again in Roscommon.

Like many houses in rural Ireland their old wireless was perched high in the corner of the kitchen on a shelf over the television. That Christmas was a milestone for her because it was then for the first time she was able to adjust the volume of the radio whenever that song came on – albeit by climbing on a chair. To this day Joe Dolan is the voice which Susan most associates with Christmas.

Christmas back then really began in earnest on "Big Saturday", the Saturday before the holiday, when the family journeyed into town to "bring home the Christmas". It was far and away the busiest day in the town, a fascinating mixture of the festive spirit and hard-nosed business.

The market square was buzzing with the "making of the deal", an event which inevitably provoked heated argument, exaggerated claims and affected disinterest and which ended either in stubborn resistance or with warm handshakes and "Gawd Bless you Mam and a happy Christmas to you and yours." The three items sold on the square were geese, turkeys and Christmas trees. The trees were subjected to intense scrutiny: all trees had to be the genuine article, the faintest suggestion of anything artificial was regarded as nothing less than sacrilege.

There was the obligatory excursion to the friary for Mass preceded by confession for which people queued interminably. On the window-ledges huge, white candles flickered slightly as a draught touched them, then shone as brightly as before. Despite the solemnity of the Mass the smell of incense smelt more beautiful than a springtime primrose.

The main shops were then visited. The heady exotic smell of spices and dried fruit, the striped pink and white sugar sticks, the gooey, twisty lengths of black liquorices, the golden candied fruits, the coloured jugs of red jam, the mysterious bulging packets were enticing promises of bliss to come. The prices of the most important items were carefully collated, before necessities as well as luxuries were purchased, stretching family financial resources to the very limit. A high level of skill was needed to fit all the ingredients for the Christmas feast into the boot of the car. Records became an ever more popular Christmas present.

The highlight of the day was a visit to the biggest shop in town to see Santa Claus. Sometimes she emerged from the excursion with a face as sad as a flooded meadow when she did not get the quality of present she hoped for.

Big Saturday was her substitute for going to Dublin on the 8th of December. That was the day Dublin was invaded by the culchies for the serious business of Christmas shopping. This was not as easy as it sounded, as all the better off people in rural Ireland had congregated in Dublin for the same purpose and all had targeted the prestigious shops like Clerys to make their purchases. The shop doors were continually opening, with the steady flow of bargain hunters, though some were there only to browse. There was barely room to sneeze. Once she travelled to Dublin on that day with her mother to visit her father in St Vincent's hospital. They travelled by train from Athlone in the morning darkness, an event in itself, with the stops in all the little towns and the commuters coming and going like buzzing bees, the struts, smoke and sparks as the powerful engine clickety-clacked to the capital city. The lucky ones grabbed the window seat and marvelled at the flashing world as the sky got lighter until it was broad daylight. This was something special, like a trip to Fairyland, a glorious treat that would repay all the weeks of being good. The enduring image was always of the Christmas lights. The simplicity of the lights was were focused on the "big smoke".

In her parish the only occasion when international events had impacted on local affairs was when a neighbour's cousin, world boxing champion Paul Pender came on holidays to the village a few years earlier. One of Susan's clearest memories of her first year in primary school was looking at all the pictures on the wall that had been taken when he walked amongst the villagers.

Pender's relative and all his family basked in the glory of his triumph. Nobody else in the county, probably even in the whole country could boast such an illustrious cousin. They promptly moved up a few steps in the social hierarchy. It always amused Susan when she heard people saying that unlike the British we do not have a class system. That's not true because we have something much more subtle. In rural Ireland there was a very definite hierarchy which kept everybody in their preordained niche. The only way to break free from your appointed status was to move out.

On Big Saturday night the decorations were always put up. The Christmas tree was normally the first to be decorated. After great debate the nicest cards the family had received were selected and exhibited on the mantelpiece amidst a sea of tinsel and holly. They cheated by putting two rows of string across the ceiling and hanging up the nicest cards from previous years. A turnip was carefully chosen to play reluctant host to a tall white Christmas candle, which was neatly adorned with sprigs of red berry holly and dispatched on the kitchen window-sill. Writing to Santa was another important task for that evening.

Susan parcelled her small presents, wrote cards, showing old world people in eighteenth and nineteenth century clothes walking about snowy landscapes. The tree was to be decked out with lovely stars, bobbles, red and green and gold, crisscrossing in a kaleidoscopic display of colour. On the branches were little candles never to be lit because her mother was afraid of fire. On the top of the tree was a tin foil star. There were little silver balls, lights like tiny stars and pale-coloured tinsel threaded among the branches. Near the top of the tree was strung a row of crinkled silver papier-mâché bells, each one with a clapper made from a varnished nut. Round the bottom were set boxes of presents done up in pretty paper tied with red ribbon. The record player was brought out and they always had a particular song for each task – though looking back on it now one of them, Eleanor Rigby, was totally inappropriate:

That night too the goose which was to form the main course for the Christmas dinner was plucked and left hanging on the back of the shed door outside. Disaster struck one night when a mini storm caused the door to open, allowing their two cats to enter. By the following morning, the goose looked rather anaemic. A crisis was averted when a neighbour gave the family one of his geese, in return for a few bags of turnips. Susan often wondered if in the middle of the fourth century, when Pope Julius I decided that Christ was born on the 25th of December in the year 0, he could have foreseen the implications of this date for turkeys and geese in the years to come.

The next evening was always the time for setting up the crib. This task was conducted with an air of great solemnity. The shepherds and the angels, the ox and the ass were all carefully wrapped in old newspaper to preserve their bright colours. All this was stored in a box in the loft in the outside shed. A winding staircase led up through what appeared as an extraneous round tower and there was the most fantastic collection of bric-á-brac and memorabilia collected in her grandfather's lifetime. Dust and debris were everywhere, stirred by a rat's foot or looting mice, from year to year. The task was normally rushed to make sure they didn't miss a second of the undisputed most popular programme in rural Ireland The Riordans.

The largely rural audience who watched the Riordans were once said by one smart alec to be afflicted with a "firago of feeblemindedness". And yet these people were in many ways very sophisticated as was evident in the way they used language. It took real skill to disassemble the easy platitudes and decipher their real meaning. Speaking about a dead priest in rural Ireland for example was an artform which a Ph.D student in Psycholinguistics would have found practically impossible. "He was careful with money" meant that he was a reincarnation of Scrooge.

On the other hand: "Sure he had no interest in money" said that he had allowed the Church and school to fall into rack and ruin. Worse still was "God bless him, the poor man put a lot of work into his sermons". This was a dead giveaway. These sermons went on and on like a transatlantic oceanliner. The greatest depth of feeling was evident in an apparently casual remark: "He didn't suffer fools gladly" which revealed that nobody but nobody could get on with him. The poor priest just could not win.

At Mass the Sunday before Christmas there was a crush of people. The attendance was swelled by immigrants home from Christmas, a welcome respite for families divided by economic necessity. Christmas was a time of delirious reunions as trains and buses to Athlone and Roscommon brought husbands, fathers, daughters, sons, girlfriends and boyfriends home to the bosom of their families.

During the last few days at school before the Christmas holidays Susan's normal timetable of Maths, Irish, English, History and Geography was suspended. A lot of new Christmas carols were learned including Scarlet Ribbons. In her innocence Susan presumed this song was a Christmas carol, even though it did not have any apparent reference to Christmas because it was the story of a little miracle and was designed to illustrate that even a girl's ribbons were a matter of concern in Heaven. Her illusions in this respect were rudely shattered when she heard the song on the radio the following summer in the middle of a heatwave.

Susan also read the nativity narratives story of how the angel spoke to the shepherds on the hillside and reported that: "they went in haste and found Mary and Joseph". Looking back now she wondered if that was the first Christmas rush!

Another important part of the preparation for the season was the making of Christmas cards. Part of this reason was economic; students could give cards to family members and relatives without incurring any expense. There was also a religious reason; at least half the cards had to have a nativity scene drawn on the cover. As a concession they were also allowed to put non-religious Christmas scenes on some of the cards. However, Susan suspected the main reason for this activity was that it kept them quiet for hours and hours. There was a bag of sweets for the person with the best card, which provided a definite incentive for them all to do their very best at a time when they were at their most giddy.

The day before Christmas Eve a great clean-up began and every room in the house was turned upside down and inside out as if very special visitors were coming. Everything was dusted, swept, scrubbed, scoured or polished, curtains were washed, and great piles of sticks were chopped and stored in the shed. On this day more than any other Susan marvelled at the hand of God in the Roscommon countryside.

The 24th was the day when she finished her 4000 Hail Marys, which she had begun on the first day of Advent. Inevitably she began her season by faithfully saying her daily quota of 156 Hail Marys, but she let the practice slip in the middle of the month and then in the final few days she had to bombard the heavens with prayers.

Christmas Eve brought other annual rituals. That was the day when the postman was invited in for a little "drop out of the bottle". It was just a small symbol of the outpouring of goodness which Christmas triggered off. In the festive season it seemed easier than usual to be hospitable – hospitality is when you make guests feel at home even when you wish they were in their own homes!

Every year, her next door neighbour, George Doyle, an elderly man who lived alone joined them for dinner on Christmas Eve. At Christmas George was melancholy, pessimistic, moody. In a peculiar way he both looked forward to the season of good will and dreaded it. He was impatient for the magic that never came for him but that all the preparations promised. Christmas was above all for him a time to be lonely. In his microcosm lay rural Ireland's universality. He remembered his family scattered all over the world, England, Australia, America and Canada. While they felt exile, home-sickness, longing and hoped-for returns that would never materialise, he was trapped in a prison of memories. His pain was the piercing grief of never being able to return to the way things used to be.

Like many elderly people in the West of Ireland who lived alone his loneliness became more intense and shrill with each passing Christmas – at times ascended to a chilling crescendo. Every year his longing for warmth and affection became more desperate. He was another silent victim of a vast and concealed cancer of loneliness, an emotional holocaust. Christmas was little more than a painful reminder of missed chances for lasting happiness.

Susan remembered his moustache white from the frothy Guinness which he enjoyed with his meal. Susan's mother always made a fuss of him when he came to them for Christmas, making sure he was comfortably seated and that his glass was never more than half-empty. She probably gave her guest more whisky and porter than was good for him.

Of course an unbelievable thrill every year came Susan went to visit Santa Claus in the local supermarket. One year in particular stands out. Armed with a shining two-shilling piece, a gift from mother, the requisite fee for the honour of receiving Santa, Susan took her place in the queue in a state of high excitement. She was very surprised to see a nun with three small children of the local travelling family who lived in a big tent by the side of the road. Every time she passed that excuse for a dwelling on her bike she was chilled by the constant chorus of children coughing.

A few months earlier a family of travellers had come to live a mile and a half away and been shunned by some of the local community. They were refused entry to some local pubs and shops. At Sunday Mass they sat together on the back seat of the Church. None of the "upright" pillars of the community would sit on the same seat as them. A few of the more superior parishioners decided to go to Mass in the neighbouring parish.

Susan was going to ask Santa for two gifts. However, her plans were modified when she got her first lesson in social awareness, hearing Santa's conversation with the youngest of the travelling children who was just ahead of her in the queue.

"Now little girl what will I bring you for Christmas?"

"Please sir, would ya bring me a nice dry blanket to keep me warm on the cauld nights?"

How could Susan possibly ask for two presents after that? She did not complain when she discovered that she had got poor value for her two shillings when Santa handed her a cheap-looking colouring book.

On the night before Christmas freshly cut ivy and red-berried holly were twined about the hanging cords of the pictures on the wall. A tin of biscuits was passed among all family members, bringing a tangible air of goodwill to the household. Any disappointment about missing the nicest chocolate ones was carefully disguised. The biscuits never made it past Christmas Eve. It was a tradition every year that the tin would find a place in the corner of the back kitchen. The empty biscuit tin became known as the "hen's bucket" and all food waste, sour milk, tea leaves, egg shells and potato skins ended up there. Their next destination was to be breakfast for either their hens or ducks. Every good customer in the local post office-cum-grocer-cum-newsagent got a tin of biscuits and a calendar. It was a gesture of appreciation for patronage during the year.

In dark's dull density, the curtains were stripped off the windows and a single candle was put to burn in each sill till the morning. When the rosary was said, the children were dispatched to an early night in bed, no dissenting voice was raised. The back door remained unlocked whatever the weather, so that there was no danger of Mary and Joseph going astray in their search for a resting place. Across the fields the houses glittered, the light from their candles like jewelled pin-points in the darkness.

Torn by longings she was unable to assuage Susan was incapable of settling. Anticipation was always the keenest pleasure. Bursting with impatience, she resolved to stay awake all night, to sneak a peep through the bannister, to catch a glimpse of Santa's red cloak.

The stockings were not to be touched until after the Christmas dinner. Then the presents were pulled out and examined with squeaks of delight and excitement, muffled as far as possible to let her mother have her customary snooze on the chair.

On Christmas morning Susan woke early, long before the first faint vestiges of light illuminated the specklings of frost on the hard ground. As she pulled back the curtains she was compelled to watch the world take shape despite her haste. The faint horizontal threads of clouds were growing a fiercer red against the still grey sky, the streaks intensified to scarlet and to orange and to gold, until the whole sky was a breath-taking symphony of colour. Sunrise so rose her spirits that she could later easily understand why dawn worship had been a powerful primitive belief.

Then she rushed downstairs, drawn as if by a magnet to the place under the Christmas tree, where hopefully Santa Claus had neatly piled her presents. Competition was intense as to who was to be the first to make the discovery, to shriek out: "He came, He came!" the excitement transmitting like electricity; the shining faces a fitting reward to the idea of Santa. This was a time of mystery, magic, hope and above all innocence.

At Mass the priest wore his best gold and white embroidered vestments, and the pale wax candles on the altar gleamed amid the lilies. The pungent scent of greenery mingled with the waxy smell of burning candles. The final candle in the advent wreath was lit ceremoniously. So many of her images of Christ are etched in light, the silver of frost and moonlight, the shining Star of Bethlehem guarding the Magi and the radiance of the lighted candles.

Then a solo rendering Silent Night that was so beautiful it worked a minor miracle and hushed all the coughing and shuffling. The piece de resistance was the choir's version of a timeless classic: When a child is born.

The later morning hours ran on to the day's highlight, Christmas dinner, roast goose with ham and potato stuffing. The dessert was to be Christmas pudding boiled in liquid blue flames from a tablespoonful of brandy heated over a candle, and mince pies. After Mass, preparations for the Christmas dinner began in earnest. A special tablecloth was taken out from under its hiding place and the best china and delph were rescued from the top shelf in the cupboard. The atmosphere was as Dickensian as Scrooge after the ghosts. After the feast the Christmas parcels from relatives were undone. Susan's mother made a list of distant donors so that she could write thank-you letters the following day.

When the novelty of the toys wore off and she had watched the Abbot and Costello film on television Susan devoured her new reading material. Unusually a fire was put in the parlour. Although the light was off, the crickle crackle fire provided leaping flames, dancing shadows and a rosy glow.

Her joy was compounded when her mother came in to tell her that their cow had displayed a commendable empathy with the spirit of the season by deciding to bring her beautiful healthy young calf into the world. They wriggled their toes and rubbed their gloveless hands to keep warm in the cold of early night. The stars were like holes in God's carpet which allowed the eternal light to shine through. They tiptoed in their shiny wellingtons avoiding heaps of cow dung in the stable. A hoar frost lay on the fields and the hedgerows were hung with the lace trimmings of what seemed to be a thousand spiders' webs. Their cattle were huddling under creeping hedges, staring vacantly up at the slate-grey sky with their stoic eyes, as they churned the day's grass. The trees seemed to be standing and shivering together, hugging bare limbs and grumbling about the cold. A few tattered leaves, made a flimsy blanket on the frozen earth. The proud mother was still licking her newly-born calf. The calf had a red spot on his white face, so Susan decided to call him Rudolf.

Susan had so many lovely memories of her first eight Christmases. But then tragedy struck when illness consigned her mother, like her father before her, to an early grave. Susan decided she would light a candle for both her parents in the local Church.

A shaft of lightning to the east illuminated the sky. The snow had almost stopped but she had heard on the news that another wintry blast, was expected with more ice than snow. Kneeling discreetly at the back of the Church, Susan looked around at the religious imagery and especially the Christmas crib. She had long auburn hair and vibrant green eyes, her face already mature and lovely. As she watched a plump woman in too-tight jeans lighting a candle she began to reflect on her life.

After her mother had died so tragically Susan went to live with her maiden aunt, who didn't really want to be saddled with a niece who was going to be cumbersome or interfere with her party nights, all five of them each week! Aunt Clara had a bad-tempered face and her voice sounded remarkably like a dog growling, but Susan never dared to say so. She had a way of making Susan feel small, with her sarcastic tongue. She felt it was her "duty" to lick Susan into shape. Susan drew up without care or affection.

By the time she was thirteen, Susan was sulky, very quick-tempered, and flared up easily. Aunt Clara decided to send her to the local convent secondary school, where she would get a "decent education". However, Susan got into trouble easily and quickly, and was expelled within three months. Things quickly went from bad to worse, and Susan got into trouble with the law. Susan started staying out all night and got in with a bad crowd. Then when things were at their blackest, Susan met someone special.

Denis had a very serious face that could break into a really lovely smile. Susan saw that smile the first time she met Denis, when she accidentally bumped into him, coming out of the shop a few months ago. He was the complete opposite of Susan. Nothing seemed difficult for him.

Susan liked Denis instantly. His most appealing quality was that he was such a good listener. He was very sensitive to all her anger and pain, just to talk to him was therapy for her. From the first time she had seen him wearing his black roll-neck sweater, dark blue jeans and a brown leather bomber jacket it was all over for her in the falling-in-love department. Her heart had been won perhaps even before she realised it. Her mouth curled into a smile at the memory of seeing him for the first time. His whole life had been mapped out almost from birth and the parental expectation was that he would take his rightful place at the Bar and progress from there up the ladder of justice. If he wanted to Denis could have done little actual work, because had he wanted he could have spent the majority of his time going through the huge inheritance he got from his grandmother.

Susan found herself being healed by his gentleness and gradually she began to change, kindness replaced hostility and sensitivity replaced aggression.

On Christmas Day, Susan and Denis had become engaged, Susan was blissfully happy.

She had made her card for Denis and written her own message on it:

I can't believe I found you
But we were meant to be
This Christmas I am here for you
And you are here for me.
No one else on earth
Could make me feel this way
And my love for you
Keeps growing
More and more with each passing day.

As she looked around the Church her eyes gleamed with pleasure and gratitude. As she thought of her first meeting with Denis she wondered: Do we see first with the eyes or with the heart?

Seventeen
A Christmas Message

WHEN I met Mother Teresa she told me this story.

'Some of my sisters work in Australia. On a reservation, among the Aborigines, there was an elderly man. I can assure you that you have never seen a situation as difficult as that poor old man's. He was completely ignored by everyone. His home was disordered and dirty.

I told him, "Please, let me clean you house, wash your clothes, and make your bed." He answered, "I'm okay like this. Let it be."

I said again, "You will be still better if you allow me to do it."

He finally agreed. So I was able to clean his house and wash his clothes. I discovered a beautiful lamp, covered with dust. Only God knows how many years since he last lit it.

I said to him, "Don't you light your lamp? Don't you ever use it?" He answered, "No. No one comes to see me. I have no need to light it. Who would I light it for?"

I asked, "Would you light it every night if the sisters came?"

He replied, "Of course."

From that day on the sisters committed themselves to visiting him every evening. We cleaned the lamp, and the sisters would light it every evening.

The years passed. I had completely forgotten that man. He sent this message to me one Christmas: "Tell my friend that the light she lit in my life continues to shine still."

It was a glorious day, with birds flinging themselves from the grassy fields and flying high into the sky, their twittering songs sweet and piercing as if they were providing their own service of Christmas carols

Eighteen

A Seasonal Judgement

ONE Christmas a judge decided to test the honesty of his friends, so he called them together for a festive feast. Not for them the dull, watery potatoes that most people were obliged to consume: their table was laden with fresh brown bread, smoked salmon and a massive dish of incredible stew, with bottles of wine and expensive cigars for desert.

It was a glorious day, with birds flinging themselves from the grassy fields and flying high into the sky, their twittering songs sweet and piercing as if they were providing their own service of Christmas carols. The sounds of happy children playing nearby drifted in, along with the agitated bark of a dog, which was probably part of their game and wished it were not.

After the feast the judge asked a question.

'What would you do if you were walking along and found a purse full of money lying in the road?' he asked.

'I'd return it to its owner,' said one friend. He was a man in his middle thirties who was clearly well nourished and who sported a head of brown hair and a patchy beard. His skin was puckered in places, as though his complexion had been spoiled by a pox at some point. His clothes though were of the most remarkable quality.

'His answer comes so quickly, I must wonder if he really means it,' the judge thought.

'I'd keep the money if nobody saw me find it,' said a vast man, whose jowls quivered with fat as he munched on his meal. The judge had seldom before seen a man of such immense proportions and was delighted that he had provided him with a sturdy seat of oak, probably so that his enormous weight would not tip a bench and precipitate the others on the floor. His blue shirt was the size of a tent, yet was still stretched taut across his chest and stomach, and a series of wobbling chins cascaded down the front of it. Even the process of sitting and devouring a magnificently, monstrous meal seemed too much exercise; beads of sweat broke out across his face and oozed into the greasy strands of mousy-brown hair that sprouted from his neck.

'He has a frank tongue, but a wicked heart,' the judge told himself.

'Well,' said a third friend with large, sorrowful eyes and a mouth that drooped open in a flaccid gape, much like the goldfish in the judge's bowl, 'to be honest as it's Christmas, I believe I'd be tempted to keep it. So I would pray to God that He give me the strength to resist such temptation and do the right thing.'

'Aha,' thought the judge. 'Here is the man I would trust.'

Nineteen

Unto Us
A Child Is Born

IT is the first Christmas and Jesus is being born in a stable at Bethlehem. Always first with breaking stories Sky News send a camera crew to cover the event. They have no religious affairs correspondent, so they send their Middle East reporter, Ocome Emmanuel to cover the event.

Ocome: Joining me live outside the stable in Bethlehem is the distinguished theologian, Adesti Fideles. Welcome to Sky News.

Adesti: Thank you.

Ocome: What is going on here tonight?

Adesti: In the immortal words of Johnny Mathis a ray of hope is flickering across the sky. A child is being born who will turn the world on its head and heal the sick, feed the poor and bring the world eternal life.

Ocome: But why?

Adesti: Put simply because God so loved the world that he is sending his only son. Tonight the Word is made flesh. One of the most important truths of the Christian faith which tonight embodies is the fact of God's trust in humanity. The Nativity highlights most starkly the full measure of human responsibility and human destiny as it is a declaration of God's trust in humankind. The unknown God who is lord of all discloses to people that if they want to know what he is like, they should look in the stable – at a human life.

Ocome: So he is a kind of religious king then?

Adesti: That's not exactly the phrase I would use myself but he will become Christ the King. This baby comes as, 'the way, the truth and the life'. He comes to bring 'the Good News to the poor.'

It is a particular kind of Good News because its truth hurts as much as it liberates. Sadly there are many cosy corners that need to be challenged and many aspects of contemporary society that stand in need of liberation. For all our talk of equal rights a significant minority of people living in our world have not significantly improved their lot or achieved legal, economic or cultural justice. Ocome: But why would the son of God be born in a stable?

Adesti: Jesus is sending out a clear signal that we all have an urgent need to respond in faith and compassion to those on the margins, condemned to the exile of solitude by the forces of poverty and indifference. From this moment on any desire to understand their plight must be informed by the gospel. If we are serious about our commitment to faith we must be committed to the oppressed.

Adesti: The story of the God who saves finds its ultimate expression in Jesus Christ. He is the liberator who saves us from sin and heralds the inauguration of the kingdom. This kingdom encompasses all of life and the all of history. Liberation from sin is universal in its scope, it is open to all and includes all forms of structural injustice. As a result of the liberating action of the person whose birth we mark this evening the struggle for a just society is in its own right very a part of salvation history.

Ocome: How are people going to respond to this challenge?

Adesti: Helping the poor is like motherhood and apple pie. Nobody could object to it. The problem is that everybody is for it in principle but for how many does it translate into practical action? We are here tonight to mark the birth of a baby. The litmus test for our worship of this new child will not be the number of nice phrases we trot out but by how we live. This is a challenge that we must confront individually and collectively. Those five words are very easy to say but much more difficult to live by.

Ocome: Adesti, thank you for your time there we must leave it and hand back to studio where, after this brief interlude, they will be back discussing the really big issues of the day. But first let's take an ad break.

*King Richard strode away
into the night, a tall, upright
figure with a military strut and
a lot of vigorous and
unnecessary arm-swinging.
His beautiful wife Tasmin,
went with him and his seven
brothers. Very soon, they were
joined by a dog, which followed
quietly behind him*

Twenty
Good King Richard

GOOD King Richard had ruled over the people for many years. At the end of his life, Richard felt that he had enough time on earth and it was time to go on to the kingdom where people lived forever. When he had sorted out his affairs he set off for the high mountain, Mount Heaven. He gazed up at the sky and raised his eyes heavenward. The clouds had parted, revealing a huge patch of sugar-spangled velvet. The stars seemed more bright than usual in the moonless sky, gleaming and flickering in their millions. A white smear hinted at the presence of a belt of stars too small to be seen with the naked eye, although his friend Philosopher Peter assured him that they were really there.

King Richard strode away into the night, a tall, upright figure with a military strut and a lot of vigorous and unnecessary arm-swinging. His beautiful wife Tasmin, went with him and his seven brothers. Very soon, they were joined by a dog, which followed quietly behind him. Insects hummed high notes around their heads, and flapping at them seemed to make them more interested in him than ever. They stung, too, and it was not long before the walking party felt as though their whole bodies were covered in itching lumps from their bites.

But the journey was a difficult and painful one in other ways too. Richard's seven brothers died one by one along the way, and after that his wife. The King was all alone then, except for the dog, which continued to follow him faithfully up and up the steep, windy road to the Heavenly City.

Finally the two, tired and shattered, stopped before the gates of heaven on Christmas morning where the celestial angels were just finishing their carol service with a rousing rendition of So this is Christmas. Richard bowed humbly there as he asked to be admitted. When he looked up at the slowly lightening landscape, he saw that a thick mist hung around the entrance, and wisps of it curled around the gates, obscuring the door from sight. He scrubbed at his eyes and wondered what the day would bring.

Sky and earth were shaken by a great noise as the father of the Gods, arrived to meet and welcome the King to Paradise. But Richard wasn't fully ready.

'Without my wife and my brothers, I do not wish to enter Heaven.'

'Have no fear,' the great God answered. 'You shall meet them all in Heaven. They came before you and are here in heaven.'

But Richard had another request to make.

'This dog has come all the way with me. He is devoted to me. Surely for his faithfulness I cannot leave him outside! And besides, my heart is full of love for him!'

The great God shook his head and the earth quaked.

'You yourself may come into Heaven but you can't bring a dog in here. Cast off the dog. It's no sin.'

'But where would he go? asked the king. 'And who would go with him? He has given up all the pleasures of earth to be my companion. I cannot desert him now.'

The great God was very annoyed by this and asked, 'Are you willing to abandon Heaven, then, for this dog's sake?'

Richard replied, 'Great God of all Gods. I have steadily kept this vow – that I will never desert one that is frightened and seeks my protection, one that is homeless, or one that is too weak to protect himself and desires to live. Now I add a fourth. I have promised never to abandon one that is devoted to me. I will not leave my friend.'

Richard reached down to touch the dog and was about to turn sadly away from Heaven when suddenly before his eyes a great wonder happened. The faithful dog was changed into the God of Justice.

King Richard waited expectantly to see what was behind the charade.

Twenty-one

Rough Justice

A FARMER and a butcher were engaged in a legal action against each other over a plot of land. The case was listed for the Christmas session.

It was a thriving town and boasted its own pottery and a lucrative illegal poteen industry. The hum of voices, the rattle of carts along the cobbled streets and the whinnying of horses could be heard long before it was first light. The lawyer had a sense of a town that had barely slept the night before as he strolled around the marketplace, watching the frenetic activity taking place in the half-light as stall owners struggled with their collections of geese and turkeys as they prepared for the Christmas markets and arranged their offerings in a way that they hoped would prove irresistible to Christmas shoppers. There were butchers stalls with colourfully plumaged waterfowl hanging by their feet, and huge hunks of meat. There was plenty of fish too, displayed in neat, glistening rows apart from a grotesquely large pike hanging across one corner, its ugly head dangling in a most unappealing fashion.

There was other livestock too. Squealing pigs, frisky, frightened cattle and serene sheep were locked in pens at one end of the marketplace, while flocks of hens, ducks and squawking chickens weaved in and out of the busy stall holders. Loud human voices added to the general noise and confusion. In one small corner, spices from far-flung lands, and the enchantingly exotic aroma of cinnamon almost, though not completely, diminished the overpowering smell of warm manure from the animals.

The first shoppers brought on a renewed frenzy of energy, and the lawyer was hard pressed to keep his balance in the whirlwind.

A musician played a haunting melody on a pipe, hoping to tossed coins by passers-by, but the lawyer wished he would play something a little more cheerful and uplifting. The tune was so poignant that he felt his throat, and he was forced to take several deep breaths when an image of his late, beloved mother sprang unbidden into his mind.

He was a man imbued with plenty of energy, and he walked briskly and purposely out to the nearby village where he had been engaged by the farmer. It was a pleasant morning, with a breeze that carried the scent of the sea that lay to the south. The sun was beginning to dip red into the afternoon sky when the farmer realized that he had been walking in circles for at least an hour, round and round the maze of footpaths. At the last moment, he stopped and spun around, gazing back the way he had come as if he was looking for signs that he had been followed before deciding to enter the farmyard.

The farmer had an unusual lunch prepared especially for him. There was a haddock in pear-flavoured jelly, the inevitable locally caught rabbits, a dish of turnips that had been roasted in butter, and a bowl of thick mushroom soup. In addition, there was bread made from the finest white flour, which was soft and delicious to eat with the creamy cheese from the farmer's own cows. The lawyer ate his fill, and then retired to the parlour to talk to the farmer who was almost sitting on top of a massive log fire and sweating heavily, and his twitching jowls were beaded with perspiration.

The lawyer said to his client in a weary tone that indicated this argument was not a new one: "I'm afraid we have no hope of winning the case."

The farmer asked: "Supposing as it's Christmas time, I sent a nice turkey with my name on it to the judge, would that help?"

"That would ruin our chances completely," said the lawyer

apparently unnerved by the glare of cool loathing shot his way by his host. Like many a man who burned with the fire of his own convictions, the farmer was tedious company once he got up on his high horse and started to hold court. But at the sight of the lawyer's glare he backed away a little, and some of his confident bluster evaporated.

When the case was heard the judge found in favour of the farmer. "I can't understand how we won," said the lawyer.

"It must be the turkey I sent to him."

"You did", gasped the lawyer resentment thick in his voice as he regarded his client with rank suspicion.

The farmer answered: "I did but I put the other fellow's name on it."

She listened to the sounds of the chaos – the rumble of panic in the voices from the village, the barking of terrified dogs and the faint hiss of blowing reeds in the mounting gale. The air had the distinct tang of salt in it, overlain with a peculiar but potent fishy odour

Twenty-two

Water, Water Everywhere

A VERY religious young woman was at home having her Christmas dinner. She was tall, and voluminous skirts swirled around thick, practical travelling boots. A veil covered her head, but several strands of white hair had escaped to hang rakishly down the sides of her cheeks. Sharp blue eyes indicated a person of character, who was used to having her own way. It may be unfair to say she was lazy but if going to bed was work she would have slept on the floor.

When she saw that her table was loaded with food she gave a squeal of delight but then her mood changed quickly when a storm came and the river burst its banks. She could clearly hear a rumble, a sharp crack and suddenly the whole of the village was full of falling stone and rising dust. Immediately her face creased with concern. The quick glance she gave the numbers for the emergency services on her mantelpiece indicated that she had put her finger on the violent interruption to her Christmas celebrations.

She listened to the sounds of the chaos – the rumble of panic in the voices from the village, the barking of terrified dogs and the faint hiss of blowing reeds in the mounting gale. The air had the distinct tang of salt in it, overlain with a peculiar but potent fishy odour. Gulls, immune to the sense of impending crisis, paddled silently in the river's shallows, ducking and pecking at the water as they ate their fill of refuse that had been dumped there. Tiny pricks of erratic light implied that people were rushing for the boats.

Soon the water was up to cover the first storey of her house. A man passed by her house swearing under his breath as he almost tripped and stumbled over stray pots and other irregular looking objects in a raft and offered to take her to safety. At first she merely regarded him with an aloof expression, as if she considered a mere man in a boat beneath him, although he smiled engagingly. With a petulant pout she started to slouch towards him. She said, 'No. God will save me.'

As the water continued to rise the woman waited in her upstairs bedroom. A man rowed by her window in a boat. He stopped and offered to rescue her although the sweet smell of wine around her indicated that she had been drinking. She replied casting a venomous glance at her would-be-saviour, who was bending over trying to catch his breath, 'No thank you. God will save me.' Her words had been addressed to her Good Samaritan but it was the rising flood that she had in her beady gaze.

The water rose still higher and higher. Her dressing table was now trapped by the flood and slumped against the wall. She recoiled as a large brown water rat hovered proprietorily in the background.

The woman had to climb on her roof to stay alive even though she cut herself badly along the way. It was only a scalp wound, which bled vigorously although there was little serious damage. A helicopter passed by and the crew offered to rescue her. The pilot, hoping fervently that he would never be dispatched to live in this place, could see that the woman's eyes were hot with anger. His co-pilot sat in open-mouthed fascination, riveted to the drama unfolding before them. The woman who was growing increasingly flummoxed, and her eyebrows were trembling and twitching in agitation shouted, 'No, God will save me.'

The rain got heavier and heavier and the water got higher and higher. An hour later the woman drowned.

Sometime later the woman's spirit met with God in the next world. Her eyes were red and swollen, and her usually clear skin was blotchy. Her appearance was not improved by twin trails of mucus that ran from her nose. God handed her a piece of heavenly cloth. She was very angry and shouted at him, 'Why did you not save me during the flood. I trusted you. I was sure you would come to my assistance.'

God calmly replied, 'I sent you a raft, a boat and a helicopter.'

Then a traveller came along who was looking decidedly uncomfortable. He was small and dark, with short hair that was plastered to his head like a greasy cap. Spindly red-clad legs poked from under a purple raincoat, giving him the appearance of a predatory insect

Twenty-three

Is The Glass Half-empty Or Half-full?

THE Wise Old Owl was sitting by the side of the road. Somewhere in the distance a dog barked and a child gave a brief shriek of laughter, and then it was silent again, except for the buzzing of flies. The sun had shyly broken the morning clouds and was blazing hotly in a most unseasonal way.

To one side, the ruins of a famous castle poked through the faded grass like broken teeth, while mysterious humps and bumps in the turf hinted of a building once fit for a king to sleep in, but that had been destroyed after a vicious war 70 years previously and immediately plundered for stone by local farmers.

Then a traveller came along who was looking decidedly uncomfortable. He was small and dark, with short hair that was plastered to his head like a greasy cap. Spindly red-clad legs poked from under a purple raincoat, giving him the appearance of a predatory insect. He stopped and said, 'I'm on my way to the big city for Christmas. Tell me what the people are like there.'

The Wise Old Owl, startled to see the depth of hostility evident in the traveller, replied, 'You tell me first where you're from and what the people are like there, and I'll tell you what they are like in the city.'

Quick as a flash the traveller responded, 'I come from the tiny town of Fake Tinsel and they are all cheats and liars.'

The Wise Old Owl sighed sadly and said, 'Alas the ugly truth is better than a beautiful lie. Those are exactly the same sort of people you'll find in the big city this Christmas.'

'Did your wife not travel with you?', asked the Wise Owl.

'I got a turkey for her last Christmas.'

'That's nice.'

'Yes, it was a fair swap.'

Not long after a second traveller came along the road. He was a portly but patrician looking and his ample bulk was perched atop a pair of ludicrously slender ankles. The owl was afraid the might snap under the weight. Looking tired he sat on the ancient stone that had once acted as a lintel over one of the castle's finest chambers. It was now a moss covered relic, half buried in grass and split down the middle, too heavy and damaged to be of use for the building. A small oak tree offered welcome shade. The traveller gazed down at the moving patterns of leaves and sunlight that played and danced around his feet. He also said to The Wise Old Owl, 'I'm on my way to the big city for Christmas. Tell me what the people are like there.'

The Wise Old Owl casting a glance full of compassion asked, 'You tell me first where you're from and what the people are like there, and I'll tell you what they are like in the city.'

The second journeyman responded, 'I come from the tiny town of Mistletoe and Wine and they are all honest and honourable people.'

The Wise Old Owl beamed a beatific smile and replied, 'Good news my friend those are exactly the same sort of people you'll find in the big city this Christmas.'

Twenty-four
Get Your Priorities Right

A FERRYMAN pushed back a brown sleeve to reveal a meaty white arm, which he flexed proudly. He was powerfully built, with large, sad eyes and hair of an indeterminate colour, somewhere between brown and grey. His demeanour was always deferential.

He was taking a learned theologian across the water for the Christmas festivities. Robins flapped and fluttered on the shore and a lazy cat panted in the distance, too lethargic even to chase easy targets.

That morning a great crowd had gathered when the theologian was asked to speak at the unveiling of the crib. The Church had been a hive of activity. After he spoke with passion and eloquence people clustered around the crib, some kneeling, some standing, and prayers of all kinds were being spoken. The theologian glanced at the faces of everybody in the congregation and saw a gamut of emotions there. Some worshippers were awkward and self-conscious, whispering their entreaties almost furtively as if they somehow imagined that the good God would never bother to listen to them and that their mere presence was presumptuous. Others had no such qualms, and their prayers were more akin to demands, often delivered with ultimatums.

The theologian had not been so absorbed in his lecture to fail to notice the delicious smells emanating from the monastery's windows – a feast of freshly baked bread from the friary's finest white flour, carrot soup, roasted turnips and potatoes, and of course the obligatory fish because it was the Friday before Christmas. These rich aromas had given the theologian a great appetite and he had more than done to justice to the rich meal that had been served up to him and he savoured every mouthful. In a priory filled with busy monks, the gentle cook Brother Bartholomew provided a much-needed heaven every mealtime and he was loved for it. The theologian entirely concurred with the monks' sentiments, and expressed his debt of gratitude to the abbot who had befriended him in his youth.

As he left he was aware that the townsfolk in on him, he turned and fled, moving surprisingly swiftly and lightly for someone his size. The townsfolk returned to their houses without a word. One lingered long enough to raise his hand in salute, and then he disappeared, too, leaving the theologian alone with his thoughts.

By the time he got to the boat it was dusk, although there was not the merest glimmer of colour in the western sky, where the sun had set behind a bank of thick clouds. It was cold, too, and people scurried along with their heads down, reluctant to be out. In the distance traders hauled their carts homeward, wheels squelching and hissing in the messy mud.

The theologian was explaining the importance of using the attributes of God and of studying the divine philosophy for the salvation of the soul. The ferryman, a simple man, admitted that these great things were way beyond him. Then he suddenly said to the theologian, unblinking eyes boring into him. 'Can you swim?" The theologian admitted he couldn't "Which is a pity", said the ferryman "because the boat is sinking".

Twenty-five

The Word Is Mightier Than The Sword

GOD created the heavens and the earth and everything in them. Words were his creative agents because words are power. God spoke: "Let it be done" and it was done. And everything he made was good.

The apple of God's eye was the man and woman he created because he had breathed into them a part of himself, his spirit. The countryside smelled clean and fresh, and the scent of soil mingled with the heavier odour of grass and fresh vegetation. The man and the woman followed a road that took them through a wood, and some of its trees seemed to have been there before time even began, they were so gnarled and ancient. A brook accompanied them most of the way, trickling between its muddy banks with a gentle bubbling sound. Beautiful blackbirds sang from the top branch of the tall oak trees, and a dog barked with pleasure in the distance.

It was a pleasant journey for Adam, and Eve found herself enjoying it, despite her anxieties. The sun was shining, and the air bracing without being overly chill. The countryside was pretty, too, with little hills tucked among ancient woodlands, and a meandering river to keep them company.

Whenever God spoke the man and the woman found His words soothing and comforting; more comforting than reason dictated they should. They smiled, as they took sips from the wine God had kindly provided for them.

The devil was jealous that God had partners to share his love and vowed to teach Him a lesson. One day when God was chatting with Adam and Eve the devil sneaked up behind him and put a bond on his tongue so that He could not speak. God could no longer talk and because His creative power was in his words, the devil had denied Him that power. It was not raining, but the clouds were low and menacing and it was crystal clear that a deluge was coming. The man and woman were astonished and closed their eyes in apparent despair.

The devil celebrated by dizzily dancing for joy. Adam and Eve were shattered and lonely. It started badly, and quickly went from there to worse. Winter came in the garden. Some of the angels sang a lament of death. Others just cried a flood of tears. Birds and animals lost all zest for living. The day turned into night. A shadow of despair hung over the celestial paradise.

The devil made fun of God and kept Him in captivity for a long time. Every hour the devil would return to taunt Him. Eventually God responded by waving one finger. Intrigued the devil asked Him if He wanted to say just one word. God nodded a definite yes.

The devil thought to himself "sure one word can do no harm" and removed the bond. Adam and Eve, pale and heavy-eyed, said nothing. God had a gleam in His eye that said He was looking forward to outwitting his enemies. He spoke one word in a whisper so gentle that the devil could barely hear Him. The word released all the forgiveness that God had been storing in his heart during his period of silence. Dawn came early, with streaks of pale blue sky showing through the clouds.

The devil tugged his cloak around him as if he suddenly found the garden too cold and squawked as icy water seeped into his boots, and then he released a string of vulgar words. His face was a mask of anger, furious that a single word should cause him so much misery. He exaggerated a shiver as he stood alone.

The word was Jesus.

Twenty-six
Something Inside So Strong

IT is said that courage is not the absence of fear, but rather the judgement that something else is more important than fear. If we turn away from a challenge once, it is so much easier to do the same again the next time, and the next. Showing some courage in less serious difficulties is often the best training for the major crises. Courage is like a muscle. It is strengthened with use.

One Christmas there was a young prince who was meandering around distant lands looking for adventure. That morning he had opened a window shutter, and watched dawn steal across the fields. His face was pale in the flickering light. First, the sky turned from black to dark blue, then to violet. The landscape became full of grey shadows, which gradually resolved into trees, hedges, fences and buildings. There was no sign of the sun, hidden as it was behind a layer of cloud, but the prince felt better once the night was over at last.

As he walked the air was fresh, full of the scent of wet grass and damp earth. A few sheep bleated in the distance, and he could hear the gurgle of the nearby brook. He walked along a pleasant track that eventually descended into a wide, shallow valley. A stream meandered across water meadows that were fringed by ancient oaks. His progress was impeded by a fence that stretched across the road. There was a gate in the middle, but it was locked so he climbed over it despite the attentions of a dog who hovered beside the gate like a malevolent bird of prey. Several hens squawked their alarm at the sudden invasion by a stranger.

He came to a town which was near a pass into a fertile valley as he was thinking about the mysteries that confronted him. He had arrived just as the Christmas service was finishing and most of the congregation were leaving in a rush, eager to begin their Christmas festivities and enjoy their Christmas meals.

Nonetheless the prince was taken aback by the poverty in the town and inquired why the people did not move into the valley. The locals told him that they couldn't because a dragon was guarding the pass and that they were all afraid of him. The prince sighed, and the townsfolk saw lines of weariness etched into his face.

As princes so often do in stories like this, the prince decided that he was going to solve the problem irrespective of his own personal safety. With a brave smile but with a knot in his stomach the prince made his way to the pass. It was accessed by a wooden bridge so dangerously ruinous that crossing the moat was an adventure in itself. The prince frowned a little but took it in his stride. With his sword waving he reached his destination. He rubbed a hand through his fine hair, feeling his stomach tie itself in knots. To his great surprise all he could see was a tiny little dragon, who only was the size of his boot.

'Where's your father?' asked the prince, his voice loud and full of self-importance. The dragon stepped forward to make a low and very sincere obeisance and said, 'I live here on my own.'

'But how can a tiny little beast like you so terrify the local people?', trying to keep the reproach from his voice, but not succeeding.

'Because of my name.'

'What's your name?'

'What Might Happen?'

Twenty-seven

Let Them Know
It's Christmas

THIS month millions of children over the world are preparing for Christmas and the coming of Santa Claus. Families gather to celebrate the greatest gift of all, the gift of a baby born in a stable. It is a time of being together and for the children of great excitement, giving and getting love and presents from family and friends. But for many children across Europe and Africa Christmas Day is like any other day in the year. Nothing special just a struggle to get through the day, with temperatures in Eastern Europe as low as -20 degrees Celsius. There are no warm fires, no trees, no Christmas pudding, no Christmas presents just struggling to get through. It is a bleak, cold day, with little hope for the future.

One Irish charity called Team Hope has made a practical response to the plight of needy children. Inspired by the Gospel stories of helping others, Team Hope is an Irish Christian international development charity, helping children and through them their families and communities in almost twenty countries. It has surpassed all expectations in distributing over three million gift-filled boxes throughout Europe, the Middle East and Africa, (South America and Asia). The charity has been supported by top Irish sporting personalities like Katie Taylor.

Team Hope's Christmas Shoebox Appeal Manager Carol Hennessey explains the origins of the project:

'The idea began in Wales years ago, at the height of the crisis in the Romanian orphanages. A family were watching a news report of the absolutely horrific conditions these children were living and asked themselves the question: what can we do? They filled a shoebox with little gifts and sent it to a child in Romania.

'Team Hope was started because someone said it doesn't always have to be this way. There has to be something I can do to help these children. Last year alone 212,002 Eastern European and African children received shoe boxes from Ireland just because someone said, "There has to be something I can do."'

Team Hope's Executive Director Niall Barry is not resting on his laurels:

'The needs are still huge and every single box is important because every single child is important. We can never have too many boxes and we'd love as many people as possible to be part of the shoebox project here in Ireland. It's something that we all can do. A child from Ireland can give directly into the hands of a child (from the East) who will get no other present this Christmas. It gives great delight, it brings hope when they are hurting and it lets them know that someone does care. No one shoebox can change the world but it and what we can give will change the lives of these children. A shoebox can help change the world for one person.'

Behind the statistics there are real stories to be told as Carol Hennessey has discovered at first hand last Christmas:

'In the run-up to Christmas we carried appeals for shoeboxes in schools all round the country and we got an incredible response from individual children and from schools. A lot of families got involved in it also.

'I travelled out to Romania to present the boxes. Although we saw squalor and poverty it was a very inspiring trip. We were welcomed everywhere we went as much for our presence as our presents. The greatest gift anyone could give these children is the gift of their time. It was an incredibly uplifting experience and it was like being Santa Claus as we handed out the shoeboxes. The privilege is to see the sheer delight that a simple shoe box and a loving smile can bring to the seriously disadvantaged children we met.'

Niall Barry sees the project as a moral imperative:

'I feel it is our privilege to draw attention to the needs of those children who are poor and oppressed. I believe that every human being from Blarney to Bosnia should be treated with respect. A wrong committed against a child in Kosovo hurts as much as if the slight took place in Kilkenny. I know that we have to do everything we can to help children in need at home as well.'

Kosovo is a good example of a destination for Ireland's shoeboxes. It sounds like a macabre plot from a novel by Charles Dickens. However, the problem of child neglect in former Yugoslavia is fact not fiction. During the 1990s former Yugoslavia tore itself apart in a vicious war, creating a very serious food shortage, prolonging and deepening the humanitarian crisis. Displacement inevitably led to the death of the weak, sick, and vulnerable people. The problems have endured as Carol Hennessey has seen at first hand:

'It was very harrowing to hear about so many children maimed by landmines and bombs. When the conflict was at its height all the world's media were there. The media have long gone but the problems remain. The war created so many problems. These people face horrendous difficulties trying to pick up the pieces of their shattered lives. It is hard to explain just how much joy a simple shoebox full of presents can bring at Christmas to a child in that situation.

'The story does not end there. The shoe boxes open doors to illustrate needs. Team Hope follows up on many situations we have discovered, in order to provide help and hope on a more long-term basis.'

Niall Barry is loud in his praise of people who have donated shoeboxes.

'We know there are many calls on people's generosity. But a little goes a long way in countries as poor as this. They need people to look out for them rather than look away. They need our concern. This Christmas if you have donated a shoebox you can be happy because you have brought joy to another child. How could you possibly spend Christmas a better way than that?'

Twenty-eight
Animal Farm

ONE of the things that bonds people together is that we all carry ghosts around with us. I carry around the memory of my grandfather, the dominant male influence in my life after my father died when I was five.

Growing up on a small farm in the West of Ireland Christmas Day was a working day of sorts. One Christmas Day we went walking in the fields to feed the cattle with the world's unnoticed beauty for company.

Nature opened up new avenues of exploration for my grandfather in his attempt to interpret the meaning and truth of the Christian experience. The splendour of creation inclined him to see a presence which hovers silently and patiently behind us. In the beauty of nature he was never so duped by the mundane routines of everyday life as to fall prey to the cold blood of boredom. He passed on that part of his DNA to me.

There was plenty of fresh air about on that cold, grey day. The lake was a mirror to the clouds. We walked gingerly towards a privet hedge where I had recently spotted a group of pheasants. The privet was empty, though a gang of geese were stamping their webbed feet nearby in hopes of scraps. Suddenly I let out a cry of horror white faced as a tear coursed its way down his dusty cheek:

'What's wrong pet?' asked my grandfather in a voice full of concern.

I had spotted a rabbit with its leg caught in a snare. She was alive but whimpering terrifyingly. Her eyes were deep pools of pain. The snare had dug deep. My grandfather delicately held the creature with one hand and tried to loosen the snare with the other.

He whispered softly to the rabbit tenderly telling him he was only trying to help. But he knew from the way it squirmed that the rabbit couldn't separate the pain of the snare from his efforts to free it. It was an intimate moment, a primitive communion with a desperate creature who needed a friend. With each convulsion the snare bit deeper.

After much wailing from me my grandfather finally got the snare wire off the leg. At first the rabbit just remained shivering. Then it realised it was liberated and fled, bruised but free. My grandfather pulled up the peg that held the snare and flung it into the lake nearby. The memory of the rabbit's fierce struggle with the snare has remained with me as a metaphor for the human capacity to inflict pain and suffering onto itself.

Has the world learned that lesson?

Twenty-nine

The Straw Doll

SEAN'S mother watched her ten-year-old son squatting, arms across his knees, eyes listless. From time to time he moved his head from side to side, as if he was following some strange, self-hypnotic inner rhythm. His blackened face, the results of weeks without washing, gave his eyes a piercing gleam, suggesting a fierce determination to cling on to life. His only clothing was a thin, torn sack.

No one knew when he had his last meal, or how long he had been coughing so fiercely. His dying aunt guessed ten days. No one had heard him speak in a week. He was not responding to conversation. His family, those who were still alive, believed he was going deaf.

Other people were hunkered down in various parts of the settlement of mud huts. His aunt, her head going bald, picked lice from her daughters' matted hair. Mourning families occasionally dragged themselves inside one of the dark and decrepit mud outhouses to pray communally for the souls of the departed. Shrieks of heartbreak from someone or other punctuated the quiet hum of the recital of the rosary. This cry of anguish was a tell-tale sign that the casualty list had risen by one. Nobody noticed any more.

His uncle, growing twenty years older with every passing day, ranted furiously, eyes bulging, about Lord MacNicholas, the tyrannical landlord who feasted and lived a life of luxury while his tenants starved. His ravings against a man who stood idly by while his tenants starved was a profound if utterly futile protest against the criminal negligence of which the villagers were victims. He had good reason to be angry. Eight of his children had died already. If anyone ever did care for those people in Ballycliff, no one was there in their hour of need.

By 1847 the village had already been visited by all the plagues of Ireland – hunger, disease and government neglect. Each plague compounded the other like a battleground of contending dooms. Fragile lifelines of aid reached only a minority of the population. In the first year there was barely enough potatoes, in the next only a trickle. Then nothing. Potato stalks withered and died. There was nothing for seed. The villagers had nothing to live on and nothing to live for.

For most of the day, people simply sat on the ground, silent and despairing. Ireland was a country with a genius for extremes, from the beginning to the end. It seemed simultaneously connected to the Garden of Eden in the landlords' palaces and to some foretaste of doomsday destruction where the peasants lived to die. Nowhere were the gardens more luxuriant or a people more miserable, a society in free fall. The inchoate tragedy was a moral test which those in power failed miserably.

Bloated bellies and matchstick limbs were the order of the day. Entire families were left shaking in the heat of the midday sun, too tired to respond to coaxing because they were in an advanced stage of starvation. Children's ribs stuck through their skins. A few were still able to smile even though they were covered in filth and scabs and there was swelling under their eyes.

Their chat was smothered by a more incessant sound, the sound of coughing. Many were barely able to walk and needed a tall stick to lean on. Mothers were very distressed as they cradled their children. In the village there were tiny children no bigger than one would expect a new-born baby to be, even though they were two or three years old.

Sean just nodded as his mother handed him his only meal of the day, a tiny portion of boiled nettles. To make the meal last it was essential to keep chewing the nettles over and over again.

His impish sister, Grainne, hopping from one foot to the other, asked for milk and potatoes, luxuries she had not tasted for an eternity. With dying families too weak to look after themselves, evidence of neglect was everywhere. There was a powerful stench of human excrement. Once carefully-tended vegetable beds, were overgrown with weeds. The foul smelling floors of the gloomy, often windowless, rooms that passed for homes were littered with rat droppings. Rats were the only growth industry in the village. A plague of foot-long rats in the commune was the final ignominy.

It was the Friday before Christmas in 1846. Only 87 people were left alive in the village. They had absolutely nothing left. There wasn't a nettle left for miles or hardly a blade of grass. The epidemic of rats and mice was over because the people had clobbered them to death with stones and boiled them and eaten them. Any cats or dogs that had been still alive were also devoured. It was going to be a black Christmas.

Paddy 'the Stormer' McManus called a meeting for everybody in the village. He said it was a choice between begging or starving. After a fierce row they decided to walk to Athlone to seek either food or a ticket of admission to the poor-house. They made the ten-mile walk in a torrential downpour and freezing cold. When they got to the workhouse Paddy the Stormer knocked at the door. The man in charge said he had no power to grant them either food or a ticket for admission. He told them that their best chance of getting assistance lay with the Board of Guardians meeting which would be held the following day in Roscommon town, some fourteen miles distant. They turned around and made the journey home. Their clothes were so flimsy they might as well have been naked and they had been without food for several days.

There was a vicious snowstorm during the night. The following morning there were five inches of snow on the ground. It was no day for walking but the next meeting of the Board of Guardians was not scheduled until the twenty-third of January. Again there was a meeting. It would be all or nothing. They decided they would risk everything and make the journey to Roscommon. As they left Ballycliff early in the morning they trudged through the snow. At first the snowflakes were falling gently but it quickly turned into a blizzard. They marched blindly in their bare feet to a chorus of coughing.

Frozen to the bone and wet, they reached Roscommon at one o'clock. Again Paddy the Stormer knocked at the door. The Guardians had just gone to lunch and refused to be disturbed. The villagers were so tired and exhausted that they slumped down outside the door. They tried to take shelter behind the houses and trees. When the Guardians had been wined and dined at twenty minutes to four one of them reluctantly came out. Already three people from Ballycliff lay dead in front of his eyes because of hunger or frostbite or sickness or exhaustion or a broken heart or a broken spirit. He refused point blank to give them relief or tickets. Their walk to Roscommon had been just a death march.

Darkness had already fallen. The snow was drifting. In some places it was already a foot high. They decided to walk home because if they sat down for long they would be swamped with snow. Their spirit was totally broken. They fell like flies on the way home. Most of them had lost the will to live. The only thought that kept Grainne's father going was the picture he had of her skipping around their aunt's house with their straw doll. There was no way he was going to let himself die when she was still around.

It was early the following morning when the survivors got back to Ballycliff. Only 23 of them were still alive. The snowstorm did not clear until Christmas Eve. The villagers spent Christmas

Day going back on the road to Roscommon, gathering the corpses. The snow and freezing temperatures had kept their bodies perfectly intact. Most were buried where they fell.

The only family who had remained were Maeve O'Hara's. It was bad enough to have little or no food but they had bad housing as well with four or five houses in a cluster together with a dung pit between them. Disease spread quickly particularly as there were only small windows in the house. Maeve decided to put in a bigger window but the landlord put up her rent within days.

She was boiling a meal of snails on Christmas Eve night when the landlord, Lord MacNicholas came to evict her because she was a few pence short in the rent. She begged him to let her cook the meal so she could give the children a Christmas meal of sorts but he would not listen to her. He instructed his men to throw the food away but they would not, they could not even look at the woman in the face. MacNicholas took the pot off the fire himself with a tongs and threw it out in the street. It was said afterwards that he used appear to her when he died a few weeks later with a tongs around his neck.

By the time Grainne's father returned home he was suffering badly with pneumonia. A relentless fit of coughing had colonised him. He was in such a state that when he went into his cabin he imagined that Mary and all the children were sitting around the fire drinking the soup. He found a new surge of energy to rush and embrace them all but there was nothing only emptiness. The only life in the house was mice and rats.

Out of the corner of his eye he saw the remnants of the straw doll he had made for his beloved daughter, Grainne the previous Christmas. The rats had torn it to bits, not that she would ever need it again. He remembered how Grainne cried as they journeyed to the poor-house when she discovered they had left it behind. He could scarcely believe that it was less than three weeks ago. It seemed like three lifetimes. There had been so much death. Then he had a family and hope. Now he had nothing but heartbreak and memories. The best he could hope for was a speedy death.

The following morning he was found stretched out across the floor. His frozen hands clutched Grainne's doll. The broken doll was directly over her father's heart. The neighbour who discovered his body saw nothing odd about his death but he could not understand why he had apparently died with a smile on his face.

Thirty

All I Want For Christmas Is You

DANNY is my best friend. In 1985 Danny decided he was going on a search for love. He headed for Roscommon's premier night club Rockfords on the Saturday night of the Halloween Bank Holiday weekend. Fifty per cent of all marriages in Roscommon back then began in Rockfords. As if to show how serious he was he bought a new shirt and some Old Spice aftershave. Whenever he was asked if he liked classical music he would always say: 'I love the music in the Old Spice ad.'

It was time for the first slow set of the night. Out of the corner of his eye he saw a vision in long black hair. He can still feel the acceleration in his heartbeat and the tremor in his voice as he asked her to dance. The song was The Power of Love by Jennifer Rush. He wondered if it was an omen.

He knew everything hinged on whether she would stay with him for the second dance. He could feel the tightness in his chest as he asked her if she would stay on. She said yes. The second song was Fergal Sharkey booming out: 'A good heart is hard to find.' Danny felt the song was a sign from God. He had always believed that the idea of love at first sight was 'a load of old nonsense'. But when Danny looked deep into her sparkling ocean-blue eyes he just knew that she was 'the one' for him. From that moment on every corner of his heart would be hers.

Eight weeks passed. On Christmas Eve he brought her to the square in Roscommon town which hosted the biggest tree in the county. Shakin Stevens was singing: 'Merry Christmas Everyone', over a car radio. Danny asked her what would she like for

Christmas. She replied immediately: 'Nice jewellery, new clothes, lovely ankle boots and a fabulous handbag.' The she asked him what he would like.

As he said: 'All I want for Christmas is you', he got on his knees and pulled out a diamond engagement ring. There were tears of joy in both their eyes after she said yes. Danny knew deep in his soul that he would he never be unhappy or lonely again.

The following Christmas they were married and held the reception in Hayden's Hotel in Ballinasloe. The sun was shining and the weather was unseasonally warm and in the conditions his new bride glowed like a princess in her wedding photos. It was if Heaven was smiling on him. Danny could not believe that such a level of happiness existed as he felt that day and could feel in his bones that he was the luckiest man in Ireland, if not the world.

Christmases came and went. Then on Christmas Eve 2015, on the twentieth anniversary of their magical engagement his wife left him for a member of the gardai.

For the next year everybody he met offered him words of consolation. Some seemed more upset that there was a guard involved than that she had walked out on him.

On Christmas Eve 2016 Danny was driving home from Roscommon when he noticed a garda car behind him. The squad car started to flash his lights. Danny went into panic. He hit the accelerator of his Volkswagen Golf and drove at ferocious speed all the way home. When he pulled into his driveway the garda car followed him in all the way.

A guard walked up and Danny rolled down his window even though he was hyperventilating and extremely agitated.

'Excuse me sir, but do you know you have been doing 183km miles per hour in this vehicle? This is very serious with all the talk there is at the moment about road safety. I am afraid even though it is Christmas Eve I am going to have to prosecute you.'

Danny's breathing was still too intense for him to speak.

I can see you are very, very distressed but nonetheless I have to ask: 'What is your name, sir?'

'D-D-D-D .... Da, Da ... Dan..... Danny,' gasped Danny.

'What is your surname sir, please? Danny. Why is that name ringing a bell for me. Oh my God. Now I know why. You are the Danny that my colleague ran away with your wife. Now I understand why you had such a reaction when you saw the squad car. You were upset about what happened that you drove like a bat out of hell. Sure it's no wonder you were scared out of your wits after what that so and so of a guard put you through. We will forget that this ever happened. Let me just wish you a very happy Christmas. And on my own behalf let me apologize that my colleague ran away with your wife. I hope one day you will forget the pain and the heartbreak.'

By now Danny's breathing was back to normal. He looked up at the guard and shook his head sadly. In a soft voice he gently whispered: 'Ah guard. You don't understand. The reason I was driving so fast is that I was terrified that you were going to bring her back.'

Those early Christians clearly understood that their King was not Caesar but the risen Jesus; that the Kingdom which commanded their allegiance was not the Roman Empire but the Kingdom of God

Afterword
By Fr Peter McVerry

TWO thousand years ago, there was a man who was called "Divine", "The Son of God", and "God from God". He was given titles such as "Lord", "Redeemer", "Liberator", "Saviour of the World" and "Prince of Peace." Who was that person? It was the Emperor, Caesar Augustus.

Caesar had conquered the known world; his victories over his enemies had saved the Empire from the turmoil of constant war and brought peace to the Roman Empire. This new world of peace was attributed to the Gods and Caesar was revered throughout the Empire as the one sent by God to bring peace to the world.

In a little corner of that empire, there came into being a small group of people who took the identity of the Emperor of Rome and gave it to a Jewish peasant who had been crucified by the Emperor's representative, Pilate. Either this was a joke, intended to poke fun at Caesar, or it was high treason.

But the Emperor was not falling around the place with laughter. The early Christians were persecuted, arrested, imprisoned and sometimes executed.

Those early Christians clearly understood that their King was not Caesar but the Risen Jesus; that the Kingdom which commanded their allegiance was not the Roman Empire but the Kingdom of God. For example, young Christian males refused to serve their time in the Roman army, as commanded by the law of the Empire, because the King they followed was Jesus who commanded a radical non-violence. Although they were often arrested and sometimes executed for refusing to obey Caesar and were considered traitors, a potential threat to Caesar, they stood firm in their refusal.

They understood that the Kingdom of God which Jesus proclaimed was not a Kingdom that was only going to come at the end of time in Heaven, nor a "spiritual" Kingdom, but a Kingdom in which they were living, here and now, and which radically altered their life on earth.

When Matthew wrote his Gospel, he tells the story of three wise men who come to Jerusalem from the east. They asked:

"Where is the infant king of the Jews? We saw his star as it rose and have come to do him homage." **(Matt 2 v 1-2)**

Now Herod, Caesar's representative in Galilee, was understandably upset and proceeded to slaughter all the male children under two years of age. According to Matthew's story, he clearly understood Jesus to be a threat. Matthew makes no attempt to explain that Herod had perhaps misunderstood the wise men, that his reaction was totally unnecessary, and that Jesus was really a "spiritual" leader who posed no challenge to Herod or Caesar. On the contrary, Matthew's story describes how the three wise men fell to their knees to do him homage and offered the gifts traditionally associated with royalty, gold, frankincense and myrrh.

When Luke was writing his Gospel, he describes Mary's response to her cousin Elizabeth's affirmation that her son Jesus was the Lord.

"The Almighty..... has used the power of his arm,
He has routed the arrogant of heart,
He has pulled down princes from their thrones,
And raised high the lowly.
He has filled the starving with good things,
And sent the rich away empty." **(Luke 1 v 46-55)**

Again, Luke makes no attempt to explain that this is to be understood spiritually or metaphorically.

When John was writing his Gospel, as an old man who had

reflected all his life on his years walking with Jesus, he describes Jesus last few hours in terms of kingship.

Pilate asks him, *"Are you the King of the Jews?"* **(John 18 v 33)** Jesus does not rush in to deny it. Instead he says:

"Mine is not a kingdom of this world; if my kingdom were of this world, my men would have fought to prevent my being surrendered to the Jews." **(John 18 v 36)**

Did Jesus mean that his Kingdom was of another world, or did he mean that his Kingdom is in this world but not of it, much as an enclosed monastery of contemplative monks is in this world but not of it?

What finally made Pilate's mind up was the crowd shouting: *"If you set him free, you are no friend of Caesar's; anyone who makes himself king is defying Caesar." (John 19 v 12)*

Pilate then brings Jesus out to the crowd: *"Here is your King."* **(John 19 v 14)**

The crowd reply: *"We have no King except Caesar."* **(John 19 v 15)**

The Gospels present Jesus as a King who poses a threat to the kings of this world such as Caesar and his representatives, Herod and Pilate. The Kingdom of God, proclaimed by Jesus, was understood to be a kingdom, here and now, in this world, but the way of life lived by those in the Kingdom of God was in stark contrast to the way of life lived in all the other kingdoms that were in existence.

However, most Christians today, if you talk about the Kingdom of God, presume you are referring to Heaven, a Kingdom in another place and another time. Traditional spirituality referred to our time on earth as a pilgrimage, we are on a journey to our true home in Heaven and urged us to "use wisely the things of earth, and love the things of Heaven," as one prayer of the Mass says.

Jesus coming "that we may have life, and have it to its fullness" is understood, then, to refer to eternal life and entering eternal life in Heaven becomes the focus and objective of our relationship with Jesus.

Such a spirituality is inward-looking, self-centred; our eyes are focused on Heaven and what I must do to get there. But the spirituality of the Gospels is outward looking, other-centred; our eyes are focused on others and how we can love them.

Perhaps it's all St. Matthew's fault. He called it "The Kingdom of Heaven". He was referring to the Kingdom of God, but in deference to the Jewish culture, within which many of the Christians to whom he was writing had grown up, he was reluctant to use the word "God" out of respect for the awesomeness and holiness of God. So Matthew uses, instead, the term "Kingdom of Heaven". But it would be a mistake to believe that Matthew was referring to a "spiritual", other-worldly kingdom. No, Matthew was talking about the "Rule of Heaven", here and now, on earth.

An Interview With Fr Peter McVerry

NELSON MANDELA, John F. Kennedy, Mother Teresa and Mikhail Gorbachev. Four remarkable people who have left a distinctive imprint on the history of the world. In an Irish context what unites this famous four is that each of them have received the highest honour the state can confer on anybody – the freedom of the city of Dublin. Only 78 people, the best of the best, from home and abroad have received this honour. It is a small indication of Fr Peter McVerry's contribution to Irish life that he is one of those chosen few. His lifelong commitment to the least, the last and the lost means that he is a prophetic voice in Irish society today.

Jesus came to a people who lived in a Kingdom where they were cruelly oppressed by Caesar and his Empire. Again, in the Kingdom of Caesar in which they now lived, the vast majority lived at a subsistence level. They lived from day to day, never sure where tomorrow's food would come from. When Jesus asked his followers to pray: "Give us this day our daily bread," this was a real prayer for them, as it is today for those millions living on the edge of starvation. For most of us, however, it is a prayer whose meaning is purely metaphorical.

Jesus talked about the rich man "who feasted sumptuously every day and was dressed in the finest linen" and who couldn't even be bothered to gather up the crumbs that fell from his table to give them to the poor man at his gate. The people Jesus was talking to knew exactly, some from their own experience, what he was talking about. And when Jesus went on to say that Lazarus would be welcomed into the Kingdom of God, you can imagine them looking at one another and nodding their heads in approval.

Their own religious leaders were telling them that they had been rejected by God and here was Jesus telling them about a God, a God of compassion, who would welcome them into God's Kingdom.

McVerry believes that Jesus is telling those who came to listen about a Kingdom where those on the margins of society will be welcomed, respected, and valued instead of being rejected and unwanted; where people will reach out to the poor, and share what they have, so that their needs will be met, instead of being ignored and despised by those who had the resources to meet their needs. In this new Kingdom, people will live in a totally different way to the way they now had to live, people will live by totally different values to the values of the society around them. In this new Kingdom, their King will be, not the brutal Herod or the warmongering Caesar, but God, a God of compassion, a God who cares.

For McVerry this man, Jesus of Nazareth, born two thousand years ago, was then, and is now, the revelation of God's hope for our world. In Jesus of Nazareth, the human and the divine have become one, forever inseparable. Other religions might tell us that we encounter God in sacred places, in temples, places of worship, but Christians believe that, because of this man Jesus, we encounter God in other human beings. "In truth I tell you, in so far as you did this to one of the least of these brothers of mine, you did it to me." (Matt 25:40)

While other religions might tell us to worship God with sacred actions, with sacrifices, and prayers, we Christians, because of this man Jesus, worship God by loving God in each other, by caring, reaching out, to our fellow human beings. "I give you a new commandment, love one another; you must love one another as I have loved you." (John 13:34)

God's dream, God's hope for our world then, is that we might love one another as God has loved us, by reaching out to those who suffer, the poor, the homeless, the lonely, the sick, the rejected and the unwanted. Jesus came to make God's dream for our world a reality. To transform our world from where it is today to where God would like it to be tomorrow requires a revolution. That revolution is the Community of Christians, which Jesus called the Kingdom of God. McVerry believes that we, that Community, have a lot of soul-searching, a lot of hard thinking to do. Does the life of this community reflect the vision of God for our world? Or would Jesus find the same inequalities, injustice and marginalisation in this community as he once found two thousand years ago? Does the life of the Christian community, and the relationships within it, challenge the values and practices of the wider society in which it exists, in a way that brings persecution and rejection from that society? Or does the Christian community sit comfortably in society, indistinguishable from it? Have we betrayed the trust that God has placed in us, have we rationalised away the Gospel to suit our own interests and comforts? Are we prepared for the radical conversion that would transform our relationships with each other, particularly with the poor and marginalized?

McVerry reminds us that we are called to listen long and hard to the Gospel, to the call of the King who invites us to transform this world through a radical solidarity with all others, to follow him who gave his life for us by giving our own lives, and everything we have and are, for our brothers and sisters. If Jesus Christ today is to offer hope to those who are struggling, who live on the edge, who feel unwanted, that hope is you and I. If we do not care and share, if we do not reach out, then there is no hope, and we will have destroyed, yet again, God's dream for our world. McVerry dares us to imagine a community where no-on was poor, unless everyone was poor, where no-one was homeless, no-one lonely, no-one sick or alone without visitors, no one in prison who has been abandoned. Imagine a community where no-one felt rejected or marginalised, where everyone feels loved, valued and respected. Would not such a community surely be the Kingdom of God on earth? I decided to tease out his beliefs more:

Q: You take inspiration from a fellow Jesuit:
'Pope Francis' emphasis on the God of Mercy (mercy, he defined, as 'opening one's heart to wretchedness') is leading us into a different understanding of our relationship with God and has profound implications for the way we live our lives – and our spiritual lives. A spirituality which focuses on what I want (getting to Heaven) and on what I must do to achieve my goal (obeying God's laws) is replaced by a spirituality which focuses on what others need and what I must do to help them achieve their goal.'

Q: Fr. Peter do you think we live in an ethical crisis?
There is a homeless person sitting in the street, begging. Passing by, I wonder whether to give him money or not. On the one hand, I feel sorry for him, no place to go, hungry, cold, bored. On the other hand, maybe he isn't really homeless, or even if he is, maybe he wants money for drugs or alcohol and I may actually be making his situation worse by giving him money. It's all very confusing.

In the Millennium, a sustained campaign was waged to abolish or reduce the debt owed by the poorest Third World countries, who were being crippled by the interest they had to pay on loans they had received from the economically developed world. The campaigners argued that this repayment was preventing health and education programmes from being funded and was therefore costing lives and preventing development. Others argued that corruption was so extensive in many of these countries and spending on arms and military so high that to simply cancel the debt would make their ruling elites even wealthier, their armies even better equipped and increase the oppression and suffering of the people, not reduce it. It's all very confusing.

Q: Can the confusion be traced to a failure of ethical principles?

Unfortunately, ethical principles, while important, are not a quick-fix solution to our confusions. If they were, there would be no problems in the world. How do we build a more just world, where everyone's human rights and freedoms are respected? Ethical principles must be grounded in the values of compassion and solidarity. What is absent in our world today is not a set of ethical guidelines but a deep sense of compassion and solidarity. Unless a person is living those values, unless a nation is living by those values, then ethical principles become, not guidelines to just behaviour, but lifeless rules to be manipulated, interpreted and twisted to one's own advantage.

Compassion is not a religious feeling. While it is central to many religious faiths, including Christianity, compassion is a human feeling that is innate in all of us. It is part of our humanity. Religious faith takes all that is most human in us and seeks to root it in an understanding and experience of a Creator God, who calls us into a relationship with that God. Compassion precedes faith. All of us, of whatever faith or none, are moved by the sight of children starving, or being ill-treated. Cruelty and sadism shock us all. We can, of course, become anaesthetised to suffering and cruelty and I think this is increasingly happening in our society. Technology has enabled us to witness the suffering of so many people in so many parts of our world that we sometimes close our eyes because the pain becomes too much. We are also tempted to close our eyes because we feel so powerless to do anything about the pain – there is nothing worse than feeling pain at the suffering of another and knowing that I can do nothing about it.

When there are only a few homeless people on the streets of our cities, we can reach out and show that we care, in different ways. But when there are so many homeless people, we tend to protect ourselves from our inability to reach out to all by shutting our eyes and our hearts. Compassion involves a desire to remove the pain from people's lives and give them a happier future. But when the pain of observing the pain of others becomes too much for us to bear, then we preserve our own sanity by switching off. And so today we have lost not so much our compassion, but our sense of outrage. For the first time in Ireland since the famine, there are today whole families living on the street because we have no accommodation for them. And yet we can spend €100 million on replacing a set of traffic lights at Newlands Cross in Clondalkin by a free flow junction, so that we can shorten our journey from Dublin to Cork by ten minutes.

The Government can put aside €130 million to refund those who have paid their water charges, in the hope that it might help them to be re-elected. We are all aware of children dying in our world from hunger and preventable disease. But where is the anger, where is the indignation, where is the sense of outrage? Ethical principles must be rooted in a deep sense of compassion, a compassion that is sometimes expressed in anger. Compassion and anger are two sides of the same coin: you cannot love someone who is suffering unnecessarily without being angry at what is causing that suffering. To act ethically, we have to continually struggle against the tendency to numb the pain of seeing others in pain.

Q: But do we need to go beyond compassion?
Compassion is not enough. We are called to go further. To go beyond compassion to solidarity.

What does it mean to move beyond compassion to solidarity? There are two limitations to compassion.

The first is that in compassion we tend to give from our excess: it is our surplus resources, our surplus time, our surplus energy that we devote to those in need. We may decide to give a donation to a charity, or we may decide to give some of our time working with people on the margins. Irish people have, deservedly, a wonderful reputation for compassion. The contributions of the people of Ireland to disasters such as tsunamis or earthquakes are amongst the highest in the world per head of population. I, too, experience the compassion of Irish people for young homeless people, whose plight touches their hearts and makes them aware of how fortunate their own children have been. Our work is largely funded by their compassion. But the first limitation of compassion is that we decide what we will give to those in need.

The second limitation is that we decide to whom we will show compassion. We choose the people or charities we will support, judging them to be more or less deserving. Our compassion may stir someone to donate generously to a charity which provides counselling services for people who suffered sexual abuse as children, but we may decide that we will not contribute to a charity that is working with ex-prisoners, presumably because we do not consider that ex-prisoners deserve our charity – even though many are in prison in Ireland today because they were unable to cope with their experience of childhood sexual abuse! Those to whom we show compassion may be chosen quite arbitrarily (such as meeting a homeless person who is begging on the street) or may be chosen for us by the media (such as the image of a child crying who has lost their parents in a tsunami or earthquake). We reach out in compassion because their suffering has touched our hearts. Our compassion is, then, a feeling of distress at the pain and suffering of another human being and a desire to do something to alleviate it, usually something concrete and immediate.

But if we wish to transform our society or our world, the challenge for us is to move beyond compassion to solidarity.

Q: What do you mean by that in concrete terms?

Solidarity is a radical expression of compassion. Solidarity is rooted not in transient feelings of distress at the pain of others, but in a lifelong commitment to alleviating the pain of others. Solidarity derives not from our sense of generosity but from our sense of justice, from an acknowledgement that we are all united in our common humanity and the pain of others is our responsibility.

Solidarity, then, goes beyond compassion in two ways:

In compassion, we choose both those whom we will support, and how, and at what cost, we will support them. In solidarity, we do not choose either the victims or our response – both are chosen for us.

First, we no longer decide to whom we will reach out. Solidarity is a reaching out to all in our world who are victims, who are poor and who are marginalized, whether we like them or not, whether we feel threatened by them or not, whether we judge them to be deserving or not. It is the suffering of others that calls us into solidarity, not the choices we make.

Secondly, our response to the suffering of others is chosen not by us, but by those who suffer. Solidarity is a radical commitment to do whatever is required to alleviate their suffering, at whatever cost to ourselves.

Thus our compassion for those who are homeless may bring us to donate generously to an appeal by a charity for homeless people – which will undoubtedly do a lot of good and alleviate a lot of suffering – but we may at the same time oppose the opening of a hostel for homeless people in our neighbourhood, on the grounds that our neighbourhood is not a suitable location for such a project.

Our solidarity with those who are homeless, however, may bring us to support such a project, if it is in the interests of homeless people, despite the cost (real or imagined) to ourselves, or to our property values. Solidarity compels us to support policies in favour of the poor which may be detrimental to our own interests.

Solidarity is a willingness to respond to the suffering of others with a love which is prepared to see my life changed, even radically, in order to bring change to those who suffer. The ultimate expression of solidarity is to be willing to lay down my life in order to bring life to others. It is a recognition that my concern for others is also, ultimately, a concern for myself; that my good cannot be achieved independently of your good; that in neglecting others, I am also diminishing myself. As the African proverb says:

"If your neighbour is hungry, your chickens aren't safe".

Compassion seeks to alleviate poverty and suffering in our world; but solidarity seeks to eliminate poverty and suffering.

Our sense of solidarity with others can help to prevent the anaesthetic from dulling the pain. To empathise with another person in their pain, to feel that pain as if it was our own, can help to keep us alert to the suffering in the world. It is John and Mary and Jane's pain, John, Mary and Jane being persons known to us, which helps to minimise the tendency to treat the suffering of others as merely a "problem". It helps to prevent the anonymity of others, others being considered objectively as the "clients" and the problem being "an issue". We need to get to know people who are poor, suffering and marginalised, to be able to see life through their eyes. People who are waiting years for an operation may see the budget in a very different way to those who are cushioned by their VHI payments. Preserving our sense of outrage through personal, direct contact with some people who are poor, suffering or marginalised makes it more likely that we will act ethically towards all those who are poor.

"Solidarity is not a feeling of vague compassion or shallow distress at the misfortunes of so many people, both near and far. On the contrary, it is a firm and persevering determination to commit oneself to the common good: that is to say, to the good of all and of each individual because we are all really responsible for all." (Encyclical "Social Concern", par.38).

Q: Are you speaking from theory or from a more personal experience?

This was my own experience when I started working in the Inner City of Dublin in 1974. I went to live there with two other Jesuits in the old tenement buildings. Each house was divided into eight flats. Two things shocked me. First the conditions in which people lived there were appalling. We had a top floor flat – luckily when we moved in it wasn't raining. The place was crawling with rats, and the rats were the size of little kittens and immune from every poison that was ever invented. In our flat, on the top floor, you just listened all night to the rats running on the ceiling, fighting each other, squealing, dragging bits of food. But on the ground floor, or the first floor, parents would tell you of waking up in the morning and finding a rat on the baby's cot.

But that wasn't the worst of it. The worst of it was that there was no sound-proofing between flats, as they were originally only rooms in a large house. We could hear the news on the TV in the flat below us perfectly clearly. Now, each house had at least one family with problems, and the problems were usually drink related. In our house the family with problems lived in the flat below us. Both parents were alcoholics, spent the evening in the pub and, about three times a week, came home at 1am and had an almighty row. They would be shouting and roaring at each other, cups would fly across the room and smash against the wall, and you would hear their 3-year old child crying in one of the bedrooms. This row would go on for maybe two hours until they fell asleep from drink and exhaustion. But the rest of the house was wide awake – you didn't sleep through this. So, imagine parents who had to get up in the morning to go to work:

frequently they wouldn't get to sleep until 3 or 4 in the morning, they would sleep it out in the morning, arrive into work late. So the employer would eventually get fed up and sack them.

And imagine children who had to get up to go to school. Again, they would get into school late, sit at the back of the class dozing off, eventually they would lose interest in school and either leave or get expelled for disruptive behaviour. It was impossible to go to school; at that time, no child had ever gone to school in that area after the age of 12. So they were hanging around the street all day and half the night, most of their parents were unemployed and couldn't give them any pocket money, so what were they doing? A little bit of robbing. And by the time they were 16 or 17, they were doing a lot of robbing and going to prison. It was as predictable as day follows night.

But what shocked me even more than the conditions which hundreds of families had to endure in this area was the fact that I had been living in Dublin for the previous 20 years, and had walked through this area regularly, but the housing conditions in which people had to live did not impact on me at all. Yes, I was aware that the conditions were bad, I thought it was unfortunate that people had to live there, but it was only when I went to live there, and experience the conditions myself, and befriend people who had no choice but to live there, that I became outraged by it all and determined to do what little I could to change it.

If our solidarity is to be "a firm and persevering determination to commit oneself to the common good," it needs to be rooted in that personal contact with some people on the margins.

Similarly, with our politicians and decision makers. If we are to build a just society, they too need to be in constant, direct, contact with homeless people, drug users, prisoners, people in poor neighbourhoods. It is not sufficient to meet "clients" in their clinics. Indeed, meeting "clients" in their clinics can convince them that they know the problems which they face. But like me walking through the Inner City, I had a "head" knowledge of the problems, but no "heart" knowledge, and only the "heart" knowledge moves us to action.

Q: How can the teaching of Jesus guide us in that respect?
Jesus did not pronounce ethical principles, he told stories about people, which enthused his listeners and outraged them.

He told the story of the rich man who was dressed in the finest clothes and feasted sumptuously every day. And the poor man who sat at his gate, hoping to get a few crumbs from the rich man's table. But the rich man couldn't be bothered. (Luke 16 v 9-26).

He told the story of the rich landowner who had a bumper harvest, and wondered what to do with his record crop. "I know," he said, "I will build bigger barns and store up my produce there and I will have enough to last me for the rest of my life," without a thought for the hungry and poor all around him.

He told the story of the workers who waited each day in the market place to see if someone would hire them, and give them a wage which would allow them to feed their family that day. If they didn't get hired, their family went hungry.

His stories talked about situations in which people were treated badly, ignored or walked upon. These were not made-up stories, they were real life stories with which many of his listeners would be familiar. The stories enabled people to empathise with others in the unjust situation in which they found themselves. The ethical thing to do was usually very clear, the ethical principles were deafeningly loud, but Jesus explained them in terms of concrete situations and real people. The discernment demanded by Jesus was based on compassion and solidarity.

"So always treat others as you would like them to treat you; that is the meaning of the Law and the Prophets" (Matthew 7: 12)

Q: Great idea, but does it translate into action?

Ethical principles have to struggle against our almost infinite capacity for self-deception. Our ability to rationalise and make decisions, which are in our own interests, while preserving the belief that we are acting ethically, is usually very apparent in others! However, we can often delude ourselves that this very common phenomenon does not affect us. My desire for comfort or for security are two frequently occurring drives which affect the decisions I make. My attachment to my own way of doing things, or my own attitudes and feelings about things, may prevent me from being objective. During the era of slavery, many God-fearing, good-living people owned slaves. Hopefully some of them treated their slaves well, as their ethical principals required. But these ethical principals often did not challenge the institution of slavery itself. This self-interest which clouds our objectivity is particularly difficult to unmask as it may be rooted very deeply in my psyche and therefore very hidden even to myself. Unjust structures, such as slavery, become embedded in our consciousness and we fail to see the injustice in them.

If I had grown up in Pakistan, I would not now be a Jesuit priest, but would probably be a Muslim Imam, or perhaps even a suicide bomber. If I had grown up in a staunch Unionist family, my mindset, my understanding of what is happening in society, and the changes that are needed, would be very different to my mindset if I had grown up in a staunchly Republican family. If I had grown up in a Fianna Fáil family, well, there are some good counsellors around!

Most of us, however, believe that we are the essence of objectivity and are unwilling to admit that we are motivated by self-interest. The problem is not bad people making bad decisions but good people making bad decisions having convinced themselves that they were good decisions. They are not acting out of malice

– indeed it would be much easier to deal with them if they were! – but out of ignorance, ignorance of the reality of life for poor people and of the effect of the decisions they make on their lives.

We see it in relations between different parts of the world, between different countries, different regions, different communities. Decisions that could make a vital, life-giving difference to some people are rejected, watered down, compromised because of the relatively minor effects or inconvenience which those decisions would have on those who make them.

Q: But why do we make such decisions?

A major part of the rationalisation which we all go on with is our unwillingness or inability to listen. We do not want our situation or our thinking to be disturbed by the contrary views of others. And so we set up mechanisms by which such challenges can be dismissed. We find all sorts of reasons which invalidate or rubbish such views. This is especially true of the views of the poor themselves, which of course challenge us the most.

If I live in the top floor flat of a building and at 8 o'clock in the morning I pull back the curtains, the sun shines in. I look out the window into the back garden and see the lovely multi-coloured flowers swaying in the breeze and watch the birds dancing on the lawn looking for worms. It seems to be another wonderful day.

But if I live in the basement flat of the same building and at 8 o'clock in the morning I pull back the curtains, nothing happens – the sun can't get in. I look out the window into the back garden and all I see is the white-washed wall of the outside toilet – I cannot see the flowers or the birds or the lawn. I'm not sure what sort of day it is.

Here we have two people looking out of the same house into the same garden at the same time of the same day – and they have two totally different views: there is a view from the top and a view from the bottom.

In our society there are two (and indeed more than two) totally different views. There is the view of those who are in well-paid, secure, pensionable jobs, living in a nice house in a nice area and whose children are going to third-level education; and there is the view of those who are living on the 14th floor of a tower block in Ballymun when the lifts don't work, who have been unemployed for twelve years and whose children have dropped out of school and are hanging around with wrong crowd. How they see the structures of Irish society and how they view the political, economic and social decisions that are made will probably be very different.

The perspective of the poor does not have any greater legitimacy than the perspective of any other group in our society or in our world. It is, like any other view, the view of a particular group who sees the world from their own unique situation. However, while it does not have greater legitimacy, it does have greater priority, simply because it is the view of those who are suffering or who have been excluded. This gives their viewpoint a uniqueness which demands particular attention. However, it often receives particular disdain – because they often lack education, and so they are written off as not having the knowledge to understand the "complexity" of reality; or because they lack the literacy skills to present their views in a way that keeps decision makers happy; or because they are perceived to be biased because of their particular problems (as if the rest of us weren't!).

It is the difficult task of continually trying to listen to the views of those who are poor and excluded, of trying to see life as it were through their eyes which sustains our compassion and our solidarity. It is difficult because it challenges us, our viewpoint, our securities; sometimes it even accuses us. And we usually do not like to be challenged, still less accused.

Yes, there is a right to freedom of expression and we should preserve that right as one of the fundamental pillars of a free and democratic society. But, in compassion and solidarity, we do not always insist on affirming our rights. While ethical principles might justify the printing of the cartoons, I would suggest that a sense of compassion and solidarity should have overwritten that right.

Ethical principles have their place. But ethical principles tend to be enunciated by the rich and powerful. Unless they are enlivened and challenged by dialogue with the least powerful, and awareness of their problems, they may become little more than maxims of self-interest. Acting justly does not depend on our understanding of ethical principles, helpful as that may be in some situations. It depends on the sort of person we are and are becoming.

Fr Peter you are a prophetic voice for troubled times. Thank you.

Christmas In Dublin Zoo

Sammy the seal was feeling lonely and sad
It was like all the other animals thought he was bad.
Nobody would play with him, nobody said hello
All the other animals in Dublin Zoo were all go, go, go.
Sammy got tired swimming alone in his pool,
He thought everyone around him must think he was a fool.
He slid on his tummy to the lion's den
But they were too busy chatting to notice him so he went on again.
He slid on to visit the giraffes with their necks so long
But when they didn't say anything to him
Sammy felt he must have done something wrong.
He visited the rhinos with their tummies so round
But they went to sleep so he didn't dare make a sound.
He went on to the elephants with their big trunks
But they were too busy eating, great big chunks.
'I must be very ugly', said Sammy the seal,
'I would love someone to think that I have appeal.
Everyone is too busy, everyone is in a rush
Or maybe its because my face goes into a flush.
Nobody notices me or likes my face,
I must look a proper disgrace.
Why wasn't I born with a face that's nice
Then I too would have friends like those three blind mice.'
Tears fell like floods down Sammy's face,
He slid back to his pool as if he was in a race.
But when he returned he got an awful shock,
There was this beautiful girl seal sitting on a rock.
She told him Samantha was her name

And she wanted him to join her in a game.
Soon Sammy was playing like a clown
And gone from his face was that horrible frown.
 Then Samantha said in words so sweet
That Sammy's face lit up like he had got the greatest Christmas treat:
'You're beautiful,
You're beautiful it's true
I saw your face in a crowded space
And I don't know what to do
You're the most beautiful animal in Dublin Zoo.'
From that day on Sammy the seal was never sad
He lived with Samantha and the seven children they had.
They spent all their days in Dublin Zoo
Bringing happiness and joy
To visiting boys and girls just like you.

A Life Less Ordinary
Jim Moran SJ

WHAT is the connection between one of the greatest legends in
Irish rugby, a giant of the Irish music industry and a Jesuit priest?
In the 1980s John Hughes sprang to international prominence with
the success of his band Minor Detail and later as the manager of
the phenomenally successful the Corrs. Ollie Campbell is described
by George Hook as 'Irish rugby's greatest number ten in the
modern era'. Both attended Belvedere College and there they came
under the spell of Fr Jim Moran S.J. who died in November 2016.

Ollie Campbell outlines the nature of their relationship: 'John
and I owe him a lot. He was a friend and a mentor to both of us and
a massive presence in our lives right through to the very end. He
instilled in us the ability to focus on our goals, gave us plenty of
confidence – but never too much – and enough back bone to last
forever.

'How else can I describe him? He was a phenomenal influence
on me as a rugby player and most of what I know about the game
can be traced back to Jim. I took from him a determination and
desire to win, even though he rightly believed that 'it wasn't
about the winning'.'

When Fr Jim went off to Chicago to study and offered his rugby
training services to a Jesuit school there, telling them of his
winning accomplishments back in Ireland. His offer however
was politely declined. So Jim took himself off to a neighbouring
Jewish school where the same offer was gratefully accepted.
Some time later his rugby team took on the Jesuit school that had
spurned him and won.

One of the buzz words in modern life is having 'a holistic
perspective'. Ollie Campbell believes that this was key to his

ability to have a huge impact on the most divergent of personalities: 'At his funeral there were five things brought up to the altar to represent his life – a Bible (he did not have an easy life because of illness but had great faith even by Jesuit standards), a rugby ball, a bunch of flowers (to represent his love of gardening), a photo of two dogs awaiting his arrival in John Hughes house (to represent his love of dogs – they loved him too, even strays), and his thesis to show his love for learning.

'His way of training rugby apart from winning trophies was to develop not just the player but the person. I was brought up in a very different time where people were not as tuned in to the culture of affirming young people as we are today. Jim was so much ahead of his time in that respect. I can still see the shock on some of my teammates faces when he had words of praise for them. It might seem small but knowing that they had his respect changed their lives. They felt empowered as people to become the best versions of themselves. He had the same effect wherever he went.'

Fr Jim's abilities as a philosopher left an enduring impression on Ollie Campbell: 'On life, he said life has no meaning – other than the meaning we ourselves give to it. On rugby he said rugby was not an end in itself it was just a means to an end, the end being the people that we meet and the friends that we keep. How right he was. This applies to any sport.'

The former Connacht rugby coach, Pat Lam, said that while it was important to him to produce better more technically gifted rugby players his primary job was to produce better people. This was an ethos shared by Jim.

A parable serves to illustrate his philosophy. After the final whistle of a big Cup triumph Jim as coach met his star player at the half-way line and they embraced:

The star player said: 'Fr Jim, this makes all the sacrifices worthwhile.'

Jim replied: 'They would have been worth it if we never won anything.'

A lot of the time winning is not about being one hundred cent better than your opponents but about doing 100 things one per cent better than the other team.

Fr Jim produced his fair share, way more than his fair share, of memorable victories and epic performances which have ignited the imagination of rugby fans. The craft and courage of this special man has added another marvellous chapter to the already richly garlanded history of a sport that demands skill, speed, strength and character. The fervent hope is that others can emulate his lofty standards. If young players in the future can live up to his trademark determination and staggering dignity it will be a magnificent legacy he has left to us.

He was a hero in the true sense of the term because when his teams performed well, *do lioigh an laoch san uile dhuine* (the hero in all of us was exulted).

The truth is it is more important to be a great man than a great coach. Jim was both. His presence will linger with us forever. The grooves in the mind hold traces and vestiges of everything that has ever happened to us. Nothing is ever lost or forgotten – a ruin is never simply empty. It remains a vivid temple of absence. His absence will always be keenly felt by his fellow Jesuits, his rugby friends and beyond.

All rugby fans were sad when they heard the news of his death. He personified what the late American sports writer, Grantland Rice meant when he wrote: 'For when the great scorer comes to write against your name, He makes not how you won or lost, but how you played the game.' Nobody did more than Jim Moran to make rugby the beautiful game. He would have in seventh heaven in February 2017 with no less than 3 Jesuit Schools in Senior Cup semi-finals!

With apologies to John Donne the sporting family is a volume. When a great player or coach dies all the pages are not tossed aside but translated into a new language. In the fullness of time God's hand will bind our scattered leaves into that library where every book will lay open to one another. All sports fans are the curator of Jim's memories.

Ollie Campbell provides the definitive epitaph for Fr. Jim: 'I thank God for this man who used his God-given genius to bring the best out of so many as rugby players and as people and for a man with such a unique capacity to enrich the human spirit.'

To quote Shakespeare:

"His life was gentle; and the elements
So mixed in him, that Nature might stand up
And say to all the world, THIS WAS A MAN!"

We shall not look upon his like again.

A Christmas Wish

Lord, make me a channel of Thy peace that,
Where there is hatred, I may bring love;
That where there is wrong, I may bring the spirit of forgiveness;
That where there is discord, I may bring harmony;
That where there is error, I may bring truth;
That where there is doubt, I may bring faith;
That where there is despair, I may bring hope;
That where there are shadows, I may bring light;
That where there is sadness, I may bring joy.
Lord, grant that I may seek rather to comfort than to be comforted,
To understand than to be understood;
To love than to be loved.
St Francis of Assisi

A Seasonal Thought

**Love is a fruit
in season at all times,
and within reach
of every hand.**

Mother Teresa

The Last Word
At Christmas

**If you want
others to be happy,
practice compassion.
If you want to be happy,
practice compassion.**

The Dalai Lama